CW00796272

ARDUINO BOOK FOR BEGINNERS

BY MIKE CHEICH

ARDUINO BOOK FOR BEGINNERS

with supplemental video lessons ▶

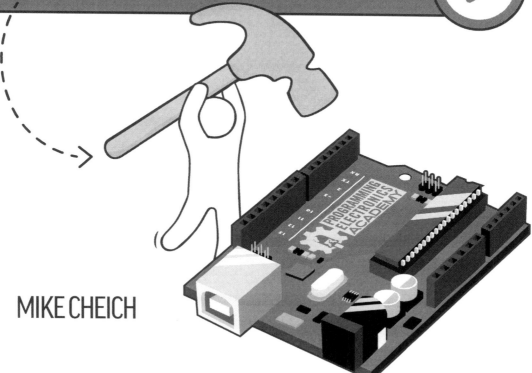

MIKE CHEICH

Acknowledgments

This book is built on the shoulders of the creators and contributors to the Arduino®.

Much thanks goes to the folks at *Fritzing.org* that enabled the easy creation of the Arduino® board images.

Ongoing appreciation to Steve Stefanidis, Rich Schanda, Josh Gilbert, and the entire Programming Electronics Academy community for sharpening this blade of knowledge through iteration and collaboration.

Many thanks to Tom Igoe, David A. Mellis, Paul Stoffregen, DojoDave, Limor Fried, and Mike Walters for the public domain code examples used in this book.

To Eleanor, Isaiah, and Samuel
- wielders of a tinker's most powerful tool -
human imagination.

Table of Contents

Online Resources..8

INTRODUCTION...**11**
How to Work through this Book..*13*
How this Book is Structured..*17*
The Arduino Community and Infrastructure.....................................*21*

CHAPTER UNO – OVERVIEW...**25**
Downloading and Installing the Arduino IDE....................................*27*
Arduino Board Overview..*29*
Arduino IDE and Sketch Overview..*31*

CHAPTER 02 – BASICS...**41**
Blink an LED...*43*
Digital Reading and Monitoring with the Serial Port........................*55*
Reading Analog Sensors and Monitoring with
the Serial Port..*67*
Reading Analog Pins and Converting the Input Value
to a Voltage Range..*75*
Fade an LED with Pulse Width Modulation Using
analogWrite()...*83*

CHAPTER 03 – CONTROL **97**

If-Else Statement, Comparison Operators and Conditions *99*

For Loop Iteration *113*

Using Arrays *129*

Switch Case Statements *147*

Switch Case Statements and Keyboard Input *159*

CHAPTER 04 – DIGITAL **171**

Blink an LED Without Using the delay() Function *173*

Using a Button with Arduino *185*

State Change Detection and the Modulo Operator *195*

Debounce a Button *215*

CHAPTER 05 – ANALOG **231**

Analog Input/Output *233*

Analog Input *243*

Calibration *253*

Smoothing Data *269*

CHAPTER 06 – ONE EXTRA **283**

Multi-Dimensional Array AKA Matrix *285*

CHAPTER 07 – THE START OF A JOURNEY **301**

Online Resources

You will also find references to supplementary video lessons through this book. These are pulled directly from the curriculum at the Programming Electronics Academy training portal.

If you purchased this book from Apple Books, Amazon, Google Play, or another reseller you will need to register your copy at *https://www.programmingelectronics.com/arduino-book/* in order to access the supplementary training videos.

If you purchased this book directly from the Programming Electronics Academy website, or are already a paid member of the training portal, then simply login to the training portal to get access to the video lessons under the *Arduino Book for Beginners* icon on the student dashboard.

The supplementary videos are not necessary for use of this book, but are designed to help you learn in different modalities. I think you'll find them quite helpful!

If you are completely new to Arduino, I highly recommend following these steps:

1. Registering the book at:

   https://www.programmingelectronics.com/arduino-book/

2. Login to the Programming Electronics Academy training portal

3. Click on the **Arduino Book for Beginners** icon

4. In the Introduction section, watch the video titled:
   What is Arduino?

INTRODUCTION

How to Work through this Book

This book is designed around extremely quick and simple-to-set-up circuits using an Arduino UNO board (though any Arduino compatible board will work just fine!)

The first thing you should do in each lesson is **set up the circuit!**

Creating the circuit should take you all of one to four minutes depending on the lesson. Each lesson begins with "Step-by-Step Instructions" to build the circuit. The written description is accompanied by a breadboard rendition of the circuit that will be useful as well.

At the beginning of each section there is a list of all the parts required for the circuit in that section. A complete list of required components for all sections is provided on the book website at *https://www.programmingelectronics.com/arduino-book/*

Once the circuit is created, **load the code!**

The circuit won't do much until you have the brains of the Arduino programmed to execute the sketch (a sketch is simply the instructions written for the microcontroller).

All the code files used in this text are available at:
https://www.programmingelectronics.com/arduino-book/

Almost every sketch example has been pulled directly from pre-loaded code that comes installed on the Arduino IDE, under File > Examples. You may notice a few changes between the code in this book and the code preinstalled on the IDE, but generally speaking they are duplicates.

Most of these programs were crafted by the founders of Arduino and are great examples of specific concepts of code.

Once the sketch is running, **read the code!**

The code is included in each lesson. Do your best to understand the program before you read about the new functions being presented. If you are lost, no sweat, it is time to start reading.

If you think you understand the sketch from reading the code – then skip the text and **start hacking!** There is no better way to learn how something ticks than to work with it.

This is how I generally approach a new sketch after I have read it and think I get the gist –

1. Make some changes.

2. Make a prediction about the outcome of my changes.

3. Validate my predictions by running the sketch and observing the circuit's behavior.

If it works as planned – I am a genius! Usually my predictions are off - but the actual behavior of the circuit serves to clarify my understanding. Rinse and repeat.

If you are the kind of person who likes to read through the full lesson before you get your hands dirty, that is fine too. I have tried to make the description of each program as user friendly as possible – but the fact remains – it can be slightly technical. Don't let the fact that you might not understand something 100% stop you from experimenting with the sketch. The more you code, the better you will code – **real understanding takes time to sink in.**

Each example will focus on a single aspect of the Arduino platform – which makes them great tools for learning. Many lessons will build on previous examples and circuits – in multiple cases you will use the same circuits but for different sketches.

You might even think some of the examples are too basic. If this is how you start to feel, then it is time for you to **make changes to the code and push the envelope of your understanding.**

At the end of each lesson, there is a "Try On Your Own" section, where you are presented with a challenge. **Take on each challenge** and make sure you save them for future use – they might come in handy some day.

As an additional resource, make sure to check out the Programming Electronics Academy website at

https://programmingelectronics.com/

There you will find tons of video lessons on Arduino programming and hardware.

All the best!

— Michael Cheich
Programming and Electronics Hobbyist

How this Book is Structured

COMPUTER CODE

Throughout the text you will see grey text boxes. These are exclusively for computer code or code explanation.

ORGANIZATION

Each chapter is divided into several sections. The content of each section is organized as follows:

KEY POINTS:

"Key Points" outlines new concepts, functions and data types to be discussed within the section.

WHAT YOU WILL NEED:

"What You Will Need" lists all the components required for the circuit. The Arduino board and the USB cable that attaches the board to your computer are not listed as they are required for every project. Also, a solderless breadboard is used in nearly every section, and thus not listed.

A list of the all the required components for the entire book can be found at *https://www.programmingelectronics.com/arduino-book/*

STEP BY STEP INSTRUCTIONS:

"Step By Step Instructions" guides you through circuit setup and loading code onto your Arduino board. A picture of the completed circuit is also included.

As you progress in the course, you may choose to skip the written instructions and just use the diagram to assemble the circuit.

THE ARDUINO CODE:

This is the Arduino code (called a *sketch*) which the section will be covering in depth. It is a good idea to read through this prior to reading the section.

DISCUSS THE SKETCH:

"Discuss the Sketch" describes in detail how the computer code is written. It is preceded by the full sketch that is used in the section. It will discuss variables declared, functions used and the over all structure and operation of the sketch.

TRY ON YOUR OWN CHALLENGE:

"Try On Your Own Challenge" is a short list of code and /or circuit modifications to practice. **This is a very important part of the learning process**. Take time to try and figure out solutions to all of these challenges.

FURTHER READING:

This section gives you hyperlinks to reading material online. Many of the links point to the Arduino reference page, where you will find documentation on all of the Arduino functions and syntax. In several circumstances, the URLs point to useful web pages on specific topics.

SUPPLEMENTAL VIDEOS:

As mentioned previously, you will also find references to supplementary video lessons pulled directly from the Programming Electronics Academy training portal.

If you purchased this book from Apple Books, Amazon, Google Play, or another reseller you will need to register your copy at *https://www.programmingelectronics.com/arduino-book/* in order to access the training videos.

If you purchased this book directly from the Programming Electronics Academy website, or are already a paid member of the training portal, then simply login to the training portal to get access to the video lessons under the *Arduino Book for Beginners* icon on the student dashboard.

The Arduino Community and Infrastructure:

Arduino is a successful platform largely due to its active user community. I say community because people in a community interact and share and grow together, and that is very much what happens with Arduino.

You want to do a couple things as you begin learning to use Arduino. First, I recommend signing up for the Arduino forum. The forum is a great resource for finding answers.

Many of the questions you have will already have been asked on the forum. You can simply search through previous forum threads for an answer. Other questions may be unique to your current project.

Before posting a question on the Arduino forum do some homework and see if the answer isn't already on the Arduino website. If you want a precise answer, ask a precise question.

For starters, include the code you are working with, the model of your Arduino board and the version of the Arduino IDE you are using.

Don't be surprised if you encounter some feedback that is negative or useless…it happens. Just shrug it off and be thankful for the majority of folks who will be nice and helpful.

PARTS

You may be interested in signing up for a Digi-Key, Mouser or Jameco account. These companies offer a plethora of electrical components that can be bought in small quantities.

I don't recommend buying an electronics shop full of parts, but when the time comes, knowing where to turn for components makes it easier.

There are also several kit companies that offer Arduino specific accessories that may be helpful in designing projects. Adafruit Industries, Sparkfun and MAKE: are great stores for these products, they offer great customer service and also provide bountiful tutorials.

PEOPLE

I recommend finding a group of local people who share an interest in microcontrollers - many times you can draw from their experience. *meetup.com* may have something listed near you, or if your town has a maker space/hacker space this may be a source of interested folks. You could always just throw something out there yourself - you might be surprised who you'll find.

These are all of course, just recommendations. I enjoy working by myself in many cases - I am just such good company!

In any case, I hope you have fun exploring the world of microcontrollers.

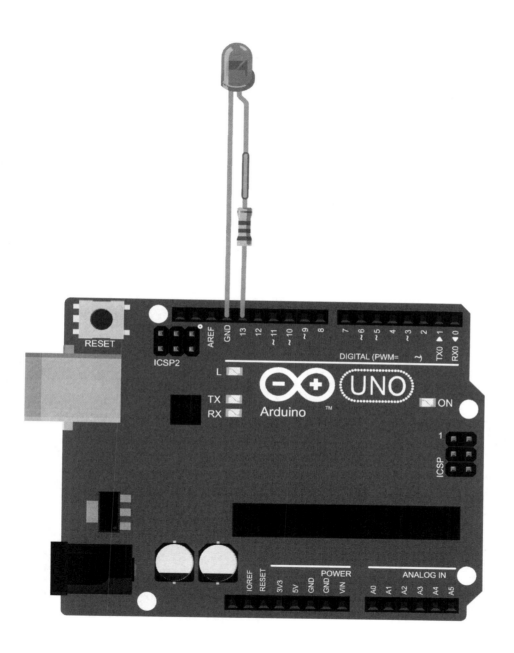

CHAPTER UNO

OVERVIEW

This introductory chapter provides the background basics for getting up and running with your Arduino board. By the end of this chapter you will be familiar with the software, hardware and the basic concept of writing code.

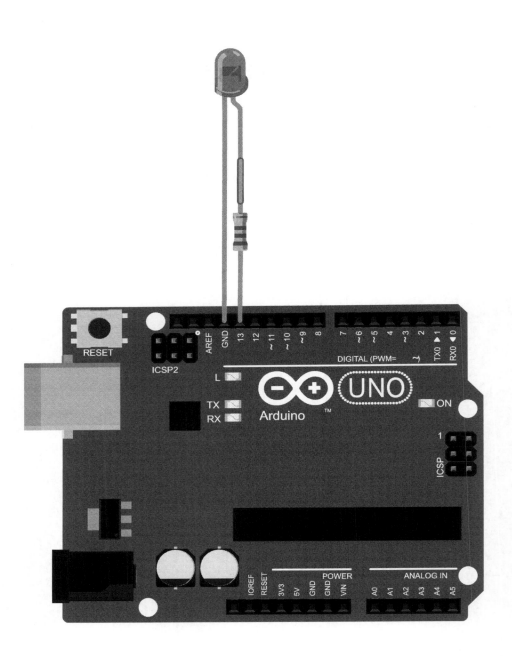

Downloading and Installing the Arduino IDE:

KEY POINTS:

1 Installation of Arduino software is relatively simple.

2 The most up-to-date installation information is available at the Arduino "Getting Started" webpage.

One of the absolute best things about the Arduino platform is how easy it is to get started. The software that is installed on your computer is completely free and designed specifically for ease of use. The program is called an *Integrated Development Environment*, or IDE. The fancy name might intimidate you but it runs just like a text editing program.

As with any software install, you may have some peculiar things working on your computer that can hinder a smooth installation. I have loaded the Arduino several times on different operating systems and have had few problems. Once or twice I had to re-download the zip file that contains the Arduino IDE, because some how or other it got messed up during the download process. You may have to install drivers yourself for your Arduino board – this turns out to be fairly easy and is clearly explained on the Arduino.cc website.

To provide you with the most accurate and up to date information about downloading and installing the Arduino IDE, I defer to the Arduino "Getting Started" page.

https://www.arduino.cc/en/Guide

They have done such a clear and concise job of describing the process, I see no reason to repeat it here.

SUPPLEMENTAL VIDEO LESSONS:

View these on the Programming Electronics Academy training portal.

- Download and Install the IDE - PC
- Download and Install the IDE - macOS
- Tinkercad Arduino Simulator

Arduino Board Overview

KEY POINTS:

1   The core technology of most Arduino boards is the Atmel ATmega 328 microcontroller.

2   Your Arduino board is resilient to shock, but don't touch it after walking across a shag carpet while petting your cat Fifi.

3   Most Arduino boards include an on board LED at digital pin 13.

What are all the components on that aesthetically pleasing blue circuit board? What does GND stand for? And what is with the "~ or PWM" mark next to those plastic lifted holes mean?

The following diagram is meant as a reference for the Arduino UNO board.

ARDUINO UNO DIAGRAM

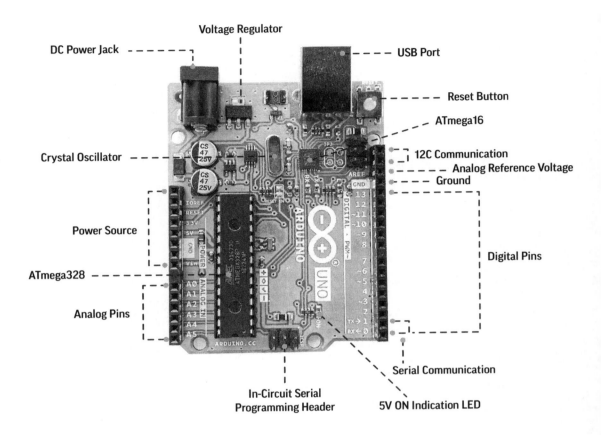

SUPPLEMENTAL VIDEO LESSONS:

View these on the Programming Electronics Academy training portal.

Hardware Overview

Arduino IDE and Sketch Overview

KEY POINTS:

1   Arduino code is similar to other programming languages.

2   An Integrated Development Environment is where you will write your programs - it is just like a text editor.

3   Computer code can look funky. It will take practice to get accustomed to the syntax of the Arduino language.

As you learned in Section 1, IDE stands for *Integrated Development Environment*. Pretty fancy sounding, and should make you feel smart anytime you use it. The IDE is a text editor-like program that allows you to write computer code for Arduino boards.

When you open the Arduino program, you are opening the IDE. It is intentionally stream lined to keep things as simple and straight-forward as possible. When you save a file in Arduino, the file is called a *sketch* – a sketch is where you save the computer code you have written.

The coding language that Arduino uses is very much like C++ ("see plus plus"), which is a common language in the world of computing. The code you learn to write for Arduino will be very similar to code you write in any other computer language – all the basic concepts remain the same – it is just a matter of learning a new dialect should you pursue other programming languages.

The code you write is "human readable", that is, it will make sense to you (sometimes), and will be organized for a human to follow. Part of the job of the IDE is to take the human readable code and translate it into machine-readable code to be executed by the Arduino. This process is called *compiling*.

The process of compiling is seamless to the user. All you have to do is press a button. If you have errors in your computer code, the *compiler* will display an error message at the bottom of the IDE and highlight the line of code that seems to be the issue. The error message is meant to help you identify what you might have done wrong – sometimes the message is very explicit, like saying, "Hey – you forget a semicolon", sometimes the error message is vague.

Why be concerned with a semicolon you ask? A semicolon is part of the Arduino language *syntax*, the rules that govern how the code is written. It is like grammar in writing. Say for example we didn't use periods when we wrote – every one would have a heck of a time trying to figure out when sentences started and ended. Or if we didn't employ the comma, how would we convey a dramatic pause to the reader?

And let me tell you, if you ever had an English teacher with an overactive red pen, the complier is ten times worse. In fact – your programs WILL NOT compile without *perfect* syntax. This might drive you crazy at first…it is very natural to forget some syntax. As you gain experience programming you will learn to be assiduous about coding grammar.

Let's get our hands dirty and introduce some syntax.

THE SEMICOLON

A semicolon needs to follow every statement written in the Arduino programming language. For example…

```
int LEDpin = 9;
```

In this statement, I am assigning a value to an integer variable (we will cover this later), notice the semicolon at the end. This tells the compiler that you have finished a chunk of code and are moving on to the next piece. A semicolon is to Arduino code, as a period is to a sentence. It signifies a complete statement.

THE DOUBLE BACKSLASH FOR SINGLE LINE COMMENTS

```
// When you type a double backslash
// all the text that follows on the same line
// will be greyed out
```

Comments are what you can use to make notes in your code. Good comments help inform a reader what the heck you were thinking when you wrote the code, or explain something that is not clear in the code itself. Here is an example of a single line comment:

```
// Needs to be a PWM capable pin
int LEDpin = 9;
```

Many of the code comments in this book have been added for clarity to the reader.

Comments will be ignored by the compiler – so you can write whatever you like in them. If you have a lot you need to explain, you can use a multi-line comment, shown below…

```
/* The multi-line comment opens with a single backslash followed
   by an asterisk. Everything that follows is grayed out and will
   be ignored by the compiler, until you close the comment using
   first an asterisk and then a backslash like this-> */
```

Comments should be written with care, and be changed when the code changes, otherwise they are lies.

CURLY BRACES

Curly braces are used to enclose further instructions carried out by a function (we discuss functions next). There is always an opening curly bracket and a closing curly bracket. If you forget to close a curly bracket, the complier will not like it and throw an error code.

```
void loop() {    // This curly brace opens
    // Way cool program here
}   // This curly brace closes
```

Remember - no curly brace may go unclosed!

FUNCTIONS()

Let's switch gears a bit and talk about functions.

Functions are pieces of code that are used so often that they are encapsulated in certain keywords so that you can use them more easily. For example, a function could be the following set of instructions...

Wash Dog Function:

1 Get a bucket

2 Fill it with water

3 Add soap

4 Find dog

5 Lather dog

6 Wash dog

7 Rinse dog

8 Dry dog

9 Put away bucket

This set of simple instructions could be encapsulated in a function that we call WashDog. Every time we want to carry out all those instructions we just type WashDog and voila - all the instructions are carried out.

In Arduino, there are certain functions that are used so often they have been built into the IDE. When you type them, the name of the function will appear orange. The function pinMode(), for example, is a common function used to designate the mode of an Arduino pin.

What's the deal with the parentheses following the function pinMode()? Many functions require *arguments* to work. An argument is information the function uses when it runs.

For our WashDog function, the arguments might be dog name and soap type, or temperature and size of bucket.

For the pinMode() function, the arguments are Pin Number and Mode.

```
pinMode(13, OUTPUT);    // Sets the mode of an Arduino pin
```

The argument 13 refers to pin 13, and OUTPUT is the mode in which you want the pin to operate. When you enter these arguments the terminology is called *passing*. You pass necessary information to the functions. Not all functions require arguments, but opening and closing parentheses will stay regardless though empty.

```
// Retrieves the length of time in milliseconds
// that the Arduino has been running
millis();
```

Notice that the word OUTPUT is blue. There are certain keywords in Arduino that are used frequently and the color blue helps identify them. The IDE turns them blue automatically.

Now we won't get into it here, but you can easily make your own functions in Arduino, and you can even get the IDE to color them for you.

We will, however, talk about the two functions used in nearly EVERY Arduino program.

VOID SETUP()

The setup() function, as the name implies, is used to set up the Arduino board. The Arduino executes all the code that is contained between the curly braces of setup() *only once*. Typical things that happen in setup() are setting the modes of pins, starting serial communication, and other things that generally only need to take place once for most Arduino programs.

```
void setup() {
    // The code between the curly braces is only run once for setup()
}
```

You might be wondering what *void* means before the function setup(). Void means that the function does not return information. Some functions do return values - our DogWash function might return the number of buckets it required to clean the dog. The function analogRead() returns an integer value between 0-1023. If this seems a bit odd now, don't worry as we will cover every common Arduino function in depth as we continue the course.

Let us review a couple things you should know about setup()...

1 setup() only runs once.

2 setup() needs to be the first function in your Arduino sketch.

3 setup() must have opening and closing curly braces.

VOID LOOP()

You have to love the Arduino developers, because the function names are so telling. As the name implies, all the code between the curly braces in loop() is repeated over and over again – in a loop. The loop() function is where the body of your program will reside.

As with setup(), the function loop() does not return any values, therefore the word void precedes it.

```
void loop(){
    // Whatever code you put here is executed over and over
}
```

Does it seem odd to you that the code runs in one big loop? This apparent lack of variation is an illusion. Most of your code will have specific conditions laying in wait which will trigger new actions.

If you have a temperature sensor connected to your Arduino for example, then when the temperature gets to a predefined threshold you might have a fan kick on. The looping code is constantly checking the temperature waiting to trigger the fan. So even though the code loops over and over, not every piece of the code will be executed every iteration of the loop.

SUPPLEMENTAL VIDEO LESSONS

View these on the Programming Electronics Academy training portal.

- Arduino Syntax Overview
- Arduino IDE sketch and overview

CHAPTER

02

BASICS

A great place to start learning is with the basics. This chapter introduces the most frequently used Arduino functions. Pay close attention to these simple programs, as the code they use is essential to working with Arduino.

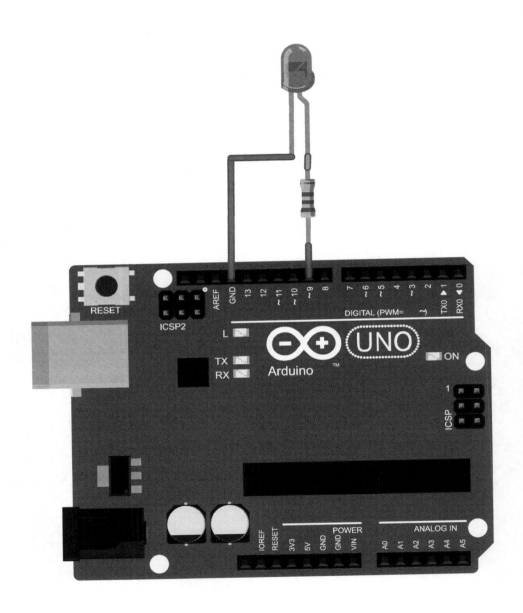

Blink an LED

KEY POINTS:

1 Blinking an LED might not seem fundamental, but it involves several key functions.

2 The pinMode() function is used to determine whether a pin will be an input or an output.

3 The digitalWrite() function allows you to control the voltage of individual Arduino pins.

4 The delay() function stops a program for a specified amount of time. The entire sketch is essentially on pause during this period.

5 An Integer data type (int) holds whole numbers and is preferred when dealing with smaller numbers.

The first program you usually write when learning a new programming language is called "Hello World". Its only function is to display the words "Hello World" on the computer monitor.

When learning to program microcontrollers such as the Arduino, the equivalent of "Hello World" is a program that blinks an LED. Guess what it is called – Blink.

YOU WILL NEED:

1. LED (1)- Any color works fine.

2. 220 ohm resistor (1)

3. Alligator clip (1) - Not essential but makes connecting the circuit easier.

4. Small and smooth rocks from a western pacific island (14)

NOTE: On most Arduino boards there is an LED soldered right by pin 13 – it is actually connected to pin 13 – so if you do not have an LED laying around (or a resistor for that matter), you can use the board mounted LED – it will blink with the same sketch.

STEP-BY-STEP INSTRUCTIONS:

1. Insert the short leg of the LED into the GND pin on your Arduino (use the GND pin closest to pin 13).

2. Connect the 220 Ohm resistor to pin 13 on the Arduino. It doesn't matter which way you connect the resistor.

3. Use the alligator clip to connect the long leg of the LED to the other leg of the resistor. If you do not have an alligator clip, twist the two leads together as best you can to get a steady electrical connection.

4. Plug the Arduino board into your computer with a USB cable.

5. Open up the Arduino IDE.

6 Open the sketch for this section.

7 Click the Verify button (check mark icon). The Arduino IDE will check your code for errors.

8 Click the Upload button (right arrow icon). You will see the TX and RX LEDs on your Arduino board begin to flash rapidly.

9 Now monitor the Arduino board - the LED should be blinking.

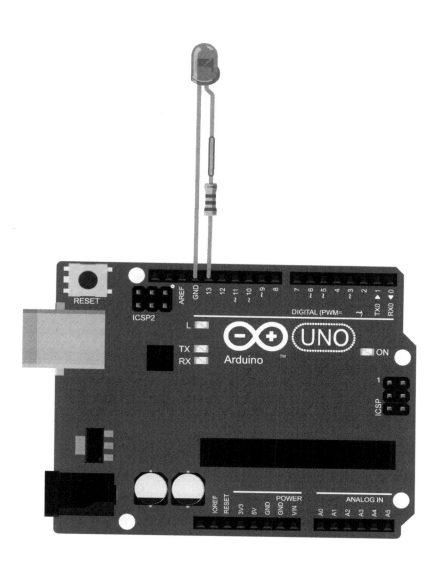

THE ARDUINO CODE:

```
/*
 * Blink Turns on an LED on for one second, then off for one
 * second, repeatedly.
 */



// Pin 13 has an LED connected on most Arduino boards.
// Give it a name:
int led = 13;



// The setup routine runs once when you press reset:
void setup() {
    // Initialize the digital pin as an output.
    pinMode(led, OUTPUT);
}



// The loop routine runs over and over again forever:
void loop() {
    digitalWrite(led, HIGH);
    // Turn the LED on (HIGH is the voltage level)
    delay(1000);
    // Wait for a second
    digitalWrite(led, LOW);
    // Turn the LED off by making the voltage LOW
    delay(1000);
    // Wait for a second
}
```

DISCUSS THE SKETCH:

On the previous page, you can see the Arduino code that constitutes the Blink program - make sure to read each line, even if doesn't make any sense yet.

Notice the comments at the top of the program. Note the use of the multi-line comments syntax /* */. It is always a good idea to take time and see what the programmer has to say about the sketch they wrote. The comments will likely be concise, describing how the program works or what it should accomplish. A few may even tell you how to connect the circuit.

Take a look at the first few lines of code that follow the multi-line comment - this is where the programmer will initialize and define *variables*.

Let's have a discussion about variables...

A variable is like a bucket. You choose what types of stuff you want in the bucket and can change the contents of the bucket as often as you like. When you declare a variable you are telling the program two things: first – the *types* of things you plan to put in the bucket, and second - the *name* of the bucket so you can refer to it later.

If you tell the program you are putting fluids in the bucket, then you can go all day filling it with beer, water, and iced tea – but the second you try to fill it with rocks, the compiler will call you out on your discrepancy. Only fluids go in a bucket defined for fluids.

To define a variable, you write the type of contents it will hold (this is called the *data type*), followed by the name:

```
// Defining a variable to hold fluid - it has a data type and a name
fluid bucketVariable;
```

Notice in the above definition statement that the word 'fluid' is a different color – that is because Arduino recognizes different data types. The Arduino IDE displays data types in orange to make them standout.

There are several variable data types at your disposal. In this lesson we discuss the *integer* data type.

You probably know that an integer is a whole number (no decimals). For Arduino an integer is a number from -32,768 to 32,767. If you try to put a number larger than that into an integer variable, the value will roll over to the opposite side like a game of Pac Man. If you add 5 to 32,767, you would get -32,764. If you subtracted 5 from -32,768 you would get 32,763.

Integer is abbreviated int. Since an integer is an Arduino data type, it will change color to orange.

```
int led;   // An integer variable called led.
```

You can name the variable whatever you want with certain restrictions. There are also a couple of good conventions to follow…

- The variable name should be descriptive of its function, for example, the ledPin variable could be the pin number that you put your LED into on your Arduino board.

- By convention most variables start lowercase.

- Variable names cannot be the same as keyword names.

- Variables cannot contain special characters !@#^&*(.

Now what if we want to put something in the bucket? Well, we assign a value to the variable. To assign a value to a variable we use an equal sign. The first time a value is assigned to a variable, it is called *initialization*. It looks like this:

```
int led;  // First we define the variable
led = 13; // Now we initialize the variable
```

Or, we can initialize and define a variable at the same time...

```
// Declare and initialize a variable with a single statement
int led;
```

That's all we will talk about variables for now. I hope you have a basic idea of how they are defined and initialized. Variables are one of the more abstract concepts in computer programming

- don't expect to fully understand them at this point - trust me that as you proceed through the lessons the concept will begin to sink in. Now on to the rest of the code...

The next block of code you encounter in the Blink sketch is...

```
void setup() {
    // Initialize the digital pin as an output.
    pinMode(led, OUTPUT);
}
```

Recall that the setup() function is in almost every Arduino sketch you encounter. Inside the curly braces is code that will only be run once by the Arduino. For this sketch notice the function pinMode() is inside the curly braces of the setup() function.

Let me start by saying that pinMode() is a wonderful function. If you recall, functions can take arguments. The pinMode() function takes two arguments – it wants a *pin* number and a *mode* for that pin. The pin number is easy, 0 to 13 for digital pins, and A0 to A5 for analog pins.

The mode is an easy designation as well, you want the pin to be either an INPUT (good for reading a sensor), or an OUTPUT (good for powering an LED).

When a pin is set as an INPUT, it *prepares* the pin to read voltages that will be applied at the pin. When a pin is set as an OUTPUT, it *prepares* the pin to output voltage - more on this later.

In this example, we want to light an LED, this requires that voltage be applied at pin 13. Therefore, we need the mode of pin 13 set as an OUTPUT. Keep in mind that setting the mode of the pin to OUTPUT does not apply a voltage, it *enables* the pin to supply a voltage once it is programmed to do so.

Moving on to the final block of code, we come to our favorite and ubiquitous function void loop()...

```
void loop() {
    digitalWrite(led, HIGH);
    // Turn the LED on (HIGH is the voltage level)
    delay(1000);
    // Wait for a second
    digitalWrite(led, LOW);
    // Turn the LED off by making the voltage LOW
    delay(1000);
    // Wait for a second
}
```

You may recall that void loop() runs over and over again. In this loop, we see two functions: digitalWrite() and delay().

The function digitalWrite() is used to apply either HIGH or LOW voltage to a pin - this is the logic level. HIGH will apply ~5 volts to the pin you designate and LOW will apply ~0 volts. If you apply a HIGH logic level to a pin that is connected through an LED to ground, then the LED will light up.

There is a voltage difference between the pin and ground, thus current is able to flow through the LED. If you apply a LOW logic level to the same pin the LED will not light up, because no current is being "pushed" through the circuit – the voltage at ground and at the pin are both zero.

digitalWrite() takes two arguments, the pin number and the level of voltage, either HIGH or LOW, as we have discussed above.

```
// Turn the LED on (HIGH is the voltage level)
digitalWrite(led, HIGH);
```

We want to start the loop by applying HIGH voltage to pin 13, where our LED is attached. In the digitalWrite( ) function we use the variable name *led* to refer back to the value 13 - which was previously assigned.

Notice that there is no need to explicitly write 13 in the digitalWrite() function, instead we are able use the variable *led*. Variables are awesome like that – they can take the place of numbers and are much easier to change and track. Every time we use the *led* variable, the Arduino will see 13. If we later decide to move our LED to pin 10, then all we have to do is change the value of 'led' once, and all the instances of 'led' are changed too.

Once digitalWrite() function has been executed, the LED will get bright – we just applied 5 volts, so hey, that makes sense. The next thing we do is delay the Arduino sketch to enjoy the bright glow of our LED. To do this we use the delay() function.

The delay() function takes one argument – the number of milliseconds you want the program to delay. In this case we want 1000 milliseconds, which equals one second.

First we said, "apply high voltage" and now we say – wait one second. Our LED will glow for exactly one second. But that gets old, and we have to stay true to the name of the sketch, so next we tell the Arduino to write a LOW voltage to pin 13 – to do this we use the same function as before, namely digitalWrite( ), but this time we want LOW voltage instead of HIGH.

Now the LED goes dark, because no current is flowing. In order to sustain that darkness we use the delay() function again for one second. Now the LED is dark for one second.

We are at the end of the loop. We turned the LED on for a second, then we turned it off for a second - what next? Once the Arduino completes the loop, it starts at the top of the loop again and repeats like a broken record.

Once again, the LED will light up, delay a second and then go dark for one second. And repeat – now you have a blinking LED – pretty cool for just a couple lines of code!

TRY ON YOUR OWN CHALLENGE:

Change the value of the delay() functions. What happens?

Change the number of the led variable to 12, and move the long leg of your LED to pin 12. See what happens.

FURTHER READING:

Go to the Arduino Reference webpage and read the documentation on these functions.

https://www.arduino.cc/reference/en/

- int
- pinMode()
- digitalWrite()
- delay()

SUPPLEMENTAL VIDEO LESSONS:

View these on the Programming Electronics Academy training portal.

- Understanding Variables

SECTION 2

Digital Reading and Monitoring with the Serial Port

KEY POINTS:

1   Serial.begin() starts communications between the Arduino and your computer.

2   digitalRead() allows you to measure the state (either HIGH or LOW), at a digital pin. HIGH equals 1 and LOW equals 0.

3   Serial.println() sends information to the serial port, which you can monitor through the Arduino IDE. You can create a textual message to tell you every time a button has been pressed, or display the value of sensor readings.

As simple as it may seem, knowing when something is either on or off can be a great tool for designing something useful.

This lesson will answer the following questions:

- Is a button being pressed?
- Has a switch been turned on?
- What is the on/off sensor status?

When you can answer questions like these, you can implement actions based on the current status – if the button is pressed do this – otherwise, do that. If the sensor is HIGH take this action, otherwise do nothing. You get the gist. But before we can implement the actions, we have to be able to track the status and the changes of the digital pins.

YOU WILL NEED:

1. Momentary pushbutton (1) - This is a button that is spring loaded, i.e. it never stays in a down position without being held down.

2. Jumper wires (3)

3. 10,000 ohm resistor (1) - More commonly referred to as a 10k resistor.

4. Very ripe banana, with peel removed (1) - Not completely useful, but nutritious.

STEP-BY-STEP INSTRUCTIONS:

1. Connect the pushbutton to the breadboard.

2. Connect one side of the pushbutton to the 5-volt pin on the Arduino board using a jumper wire.

3 Connect one side of the 10K resistor to the other side of the pushbutton.

4 Connect the other side of the resistor to the ground pin on the Arduino. You may have to use a jumper wire to make it reach.

5 On the same side the resistor is connected to the pushbutton, connect a jumper wire and run it to pin 2 on the Arduino board.

6 Connect the Arduino to your computer with the USB cable.

7 Open the sketch for this section.

8 Click the Verify button (check mark icon). The Arduino IDE will check your code for errors.

9 Click the Upload button (right arrow icon). You will see the TX and RX LEDs on your Arduino board begin to flash rapidly.

10 Now go to the menu bar at the top and select Tools > Serial Monitor. Or you could use the short cut key, *Shift + Control + M*.

11 The serial monitor window will open and will be spouting off numbers. It should be a bunch of zeros.

12 Press and hold the pushbutton – watch the serial monitor window, the numbers should now be ones.

13 If the numbers are not scrolling, make sure you click *Autoscroll* at the bottom left of the serial monitor window.

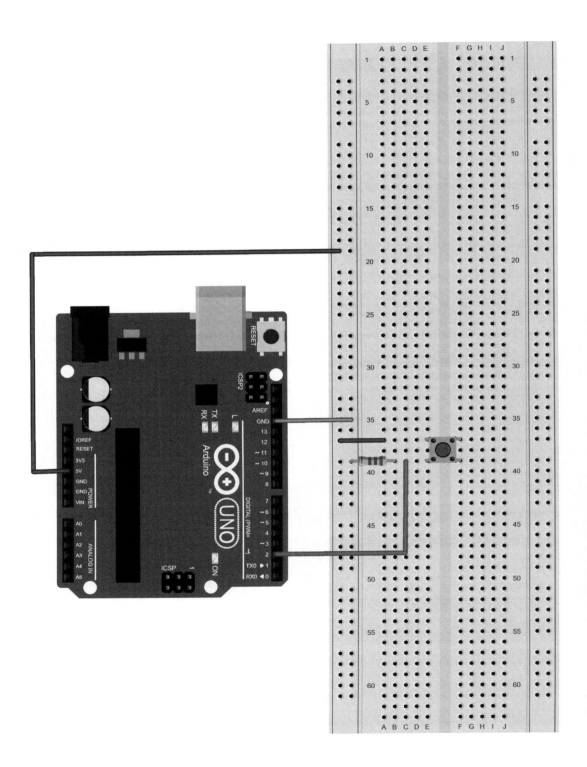

THE ARDUINO CODE

```
/*
 * DigitalReadSerial
 * Reads a digital input on pin 2, prints the result to the
 * serial monitor
 */



// Digital pin 2 has a pushbutton attached to it. Give it a name:
int pushButton = 2;



// The setup routine runs once when you press reset:
void setup() {
    // Initialize serial communication at 9600 bits per second:
    Serial.begin(9600);
    // Make the pushbutton's pin an input:
    pinMode(pushButton, INPUT);
}



// The loop routine runs over and over again forever:
void loop() {
    // Read the input pin:
    int buttonState = digitalRead(pushButton);
    // Print out the state of the button:
    Serial.println(buttonState);
    delay(1);      // Delay in between reads for stability
}
```

DISCUSS THE SKETCH:

This sketch opens with a multi-line comment containing a short description of the program and circuit. The first block of code following the comment is where we declare and initialize variables. From the last lesson we are familiar with the *integer* data type.

```
// This is the pin that our pushbutton is connected to
int pushButton = 2;
```

Notice how the variable *pushButton* is declared and initialized all on the same line. Also notice the descriptive name of the variable – *pushButton* – the variable name implies its use within the program - this is a good example to follow.

Let's consider what we have done so far – we have made a variable that will store the pin number that our pushbutton is connected to.

The next block of code we come to is the setup(). Inside these wily curly brackets there are two functions – a familiar one, pinMode() and another which we will learn to love – Serial.begin().

Serial.begin() is part of a family of functions referred to as a *library*. The name of the library is the *Serial library*. A library is just a group of functions that work toward a similar purpose. If you had a Circus library, it might contain the functions juggle(), balance() and flamingCircleOfDeath(). To access the functions in a library you write the name of the library followed by the name of the function in the library, with a period in between.

```
Circus.juggle();
```

Arduino has many preinstalled libraries. There are also many community contributed libraries that you can add. You can view all of the preinstalled libraries and some of the contributed libraries at *http://arduino.cc/en/Reference/Libraries.*

So what does the Serial library do?

The Serial library helps establish communication between your computer and the Arduino board. If you ever go to marriage counseling, you will learn that communication involves sending and receiving. Data can flow both ways. If we want to establish this communication, we use the begin() function from the Serial library.

```
Serial.begin(9600);
```

The begin() function takes one argument – the *baud rate*. What is the baud rate you ask? It is the rate at which data will flow between your computer and the Arduino. For most Arduino sketches a baud rate of 9600 is used as the argument.

That's all you really need to know about the baud rate to get started with serial monitoring. But I have a feeling you want to know more, so if you check out the further reading section at the end of this tutorial, there will be some links to tempt your insatiable desire for acquiring an understanding of all things in the universe.

The next function after Serial.begin() is the pinMode() function. We want to set the mode of a pin and what is cool about pinMode() this time around is that we are changing the arguments we pass to the function. Instead of being an OUTPUT (as in the Blink sketch), we want our pin to be an INPUT, because we want to **read** voltage at this pin, not provide it.

```
pinMode(pushButton, INPUT);
```

Here we use the variable *pushButton* to let the function know we are setting the mode at pin 2. Then we use the keyword INPUT, to say which mode we want.

Those are the only two functions in the setup() curly braces – and just as a reminder – setup() only runs once.

The next block of code is the function loop(). What do we see inside the curly braces of the loop()?

```
int buttonState = digitalRead(pushButton);
```

Whoa! What the heck is this? It looks like the programmer is declaring a variable! I thought variables were declared at the top of the sketch. While variables are often declared before the setup() function, you can actually declare and initialize a variable just about anywhere in a sketch. Soon you will see why this placement is the way to go.

Let's break down this statement. First, look at the data type and the name. We declare an integer and name it *buttonState*. Notice the variable name *buttonState* is indicative of its purpose, as we will see this variable is assigned the position of the button.

To initialize the variable, we see something altogether new – the variable is set equal to the output of a function called digitalRead(). This is going to take a little recall power on your part. Do you remember the reason for the word *void* in front of the loop() function? We had to write void because the function loop() does not return a value. But that is not the case for the function digitalRead().

The digitalRead() function returns an integer – either 1 or 0. This value is then assigned to the variable *buttonState*.

If it is 1, the voltage at the pin is HIGH, if the value is 0, the voltage at the pin is LOW. What pin you ask? Well the pin you pass as an argument in the digitalRead() function. In this case we send the variable pushButton, because we want to read the state of pin 2 (if you recall pushButton was initialized to equal 2).

All of this is in the following line of code:

```
int buttonState = digitalRead(pushButton);
```

This is why Arduino rocks – one line of code and you are on your way to dominating the world.

Now the state of our pushbutton will be either HIGH (pressed) or LOW (not-pressed). HIGH will be reported as a 1, and LOW will be reported as 0. When we press the pushbutton, pin 2 is exposed to the 5-volts from the Arduino board, this is considered HIGH, and the digitalRead() function will return 1. If the button is not pressed, then all that pin 2 is exposed to is the ground voltage which is 0 and digitalRead() will return 0.

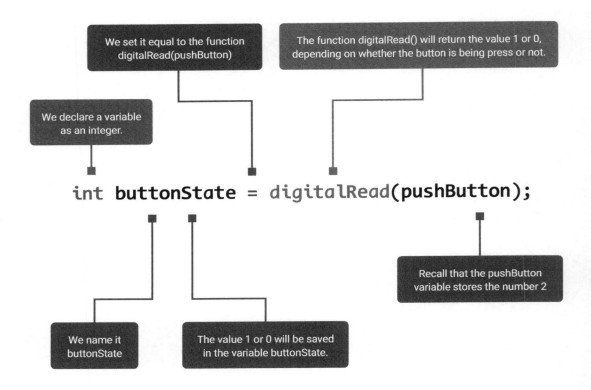

In the next line of code we return to the Serial library for another function called *println()*.

```
Serial.println(buttonState);
```

The Serial.println() function sends the value you put in the parentheses to the serial port. You can see the value displayed by using the serial monitor in the Arduino IDE. To open up the serial monitor window all you have to do is click Tools > Serial Monitor (or SHIFT + CONTROL + M). This is one way to display the data from your Arduino board.

Keep in mind that when you unplug the USB from your Arduino and use batteries to power it, the Serial.println( ) function won't do you much good. But while you are creating the circuit and the sketch, printing out values with the println() and print() functions from the Serial library is a simple troubleshooting method.

Let's cover what we have done so far in the loop(). First we read the state of digital pin 2 and saved the state in a variable. Then we displayed the state in the serial monitor window.

Finally, we used the delay() function and waited one millisecond – this allowed the reading at the pin to stabilize.

Once this was done, the loop() started again from the top. We read another value at pin 2 – we are checking every time whether the button is pressed or not pressed – this value is assigned to our buttonState variable, then we display the newly recorded value to the serial monitor window – again. And we do this over and over – hundreds of times per second.

So go ahead, press that button, watch the serial monitor window – I think you are already brewing other applications for these functions…

TRY ON YOUR OWN CHALLENGE:

- Change the function Serial.println() to Serial.print(). What happens to the output in the serial monitor window? Can you tell the difference between the two functions?

- Change the pin that you are reading to pin 3. Make the circuit change and the changes to the sketch.

FURTHER READING:

Go to the Arduino Reference webpage and read the documentation on these functions.

https://www.arduino.cc/reference/en/

- Serial Library
- Serial.begin()
- Serial.println()
- Serial.print()

SUPPLEMENTAL VIDEO LESSONS:

View these on the Programming Electronics Academy training portal.

- Digital Read and Serial Port Communications

Reading Analog Sensors and Monitoring with the Serial Port

KEY POINTS:

1   analogRead() will measure the voltage at the analog pins and return a value between 0 and 1023.

2   There are 6 analog pins on the Arduino Uno. These pins have access to the analog-to-digital converter.

Knowing if something is on or off can be extremely useful, but often you will want to know more. How bright is the light? How fast is the satellite moving? These types of answers are often analog – they cover a large range of values, not just on or off.

The Arduino handles analog inputs with 6 dedicated pins, labeled A0 through A5. These pins have access to an analog-to-digital converter, which takes the range of input values and creates a digital version by cutting up the range into tiny pieces. All this is handled behind the scenes – all you have to do is use some very simple functions and you will get what you need.

YOU WILL NEED:

1. Potentiometer (1) - Any resistance range will work.

2. Jumper wires (3)

3. Bicycle tire (1.5)

STEP-BY-STEP INSTRUCTIONS:

1. Place the potentiometer into your breadboard.

2. Run a jumper wire from the 5-Volt pin of the Arduino to either one of the outside pins of your potentiometer.

3. Run another jumper wire from one of the ground pins on your Arduino (labeled GND) to the other outside pin of the potentiometer.

4. Run the final jumper wire from pin A0 on your Arduino to the middle pin of the potentiometer.

5. Plug the Arduino into your computer.

6. Open up the Arduino IDE.

7. Open the sketch for this section.

8. Click the Verify button (check mark icon). The Arduino IDE will check your code for errors.

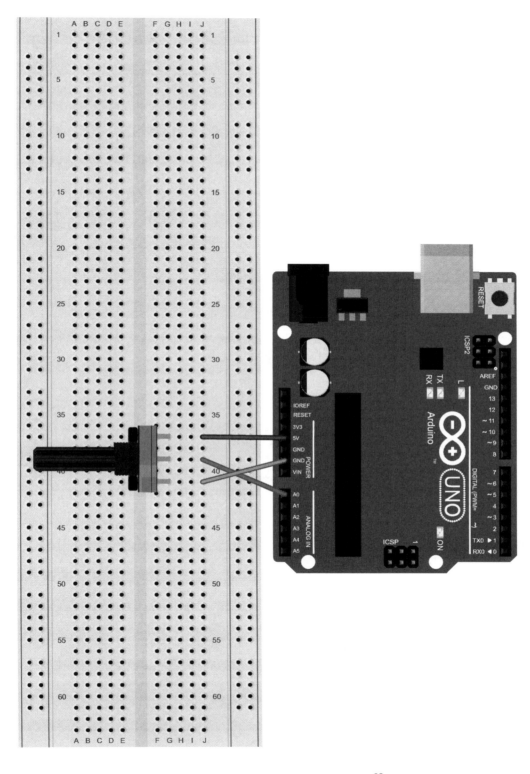

9 Click the Upload button (right arrow icon). You will see the TX and RX LEDs on your Arduino board begin to flash rapidly.

10 On the menu bar, go to Tools > Serial Monitor – this will open the Serial Monitor window – you should see numbers rolling down this screen.

11 Now adjust the knob of the potentiometer and watch the serial monitor window. The numbers should adjust between 0 and 1023.

THE ARDUINO CODE

```
/*
 * AnalogReadSerial
 * Reads an analog input on pin 0, prints the result to the
 * serial monitor.
 * Attach the center pin of a potentiometer to pin A0, and the
 * outside pins to +5V and ground.
 */


// The setup routine runs once when you press reset:
void setup() {
    // Initialize serial communication at 9600 bits per second:
    Serial.begin(9600);
}


// The loop routine runs over and over again forever:
void loop() {
    // Read the input on analog pin 0:
    int sensorValue = analogRead(A0);
```

```
// Print out the value you read:
Serial.println(sensorValue);
delay(1);      // Delay in between reads for stability
}
```

DISCUSS THE SKETCH:

This sketch starts with a multi-line comment describing the sketch and the circuit. You will probably notice that the first block of code is the setup() function – we do not declare or initialize any variables at the beginning of this sketch – instead we will do this inside the loop() function, as in the last example. Inside the curly braces of setup() we revisit the Serial library and use the function Serial.begin().

```
void setup() {
    // Initialize serial communication at 9600 bits per second:
    Serial.begin(9600);
}
```

If you recall from the last lesson, Serial.begin() takes the baud rate as an argument (this will almost always be 9600). This function allows you to setup a communication channel between the computer and the Arduino. As you may know by now, setup() only runs once, and then we move on to the next block of code.

But wait! Don't we have to set the mode of the pin we will be using? Great point!

What the Arduino does, by default, is set all the pins on the board as INPUTs unless you tell it otherwise. So in many cases you do not have to explicitly set a pin as an input using the pinMode() function. That being said – I make it a habit to do this anyway – because it makes things clear to me – and that is worth it in space and effort.

So I dare you, set the mode of the pin using the pinMode(A0, INPUT) function inside the curly braces of setup()– you won't regret it.

Moving on to the loop() function, we start with a variable declaration and initialization.

```
int sensorValue = analogRead(A0);
```

We declare a variable called *sensorValue* and we initialize it to the output of a new function. This new function is the glamorous analogRead(). So take a wild guess what this new function analogRead() does. It reads the value at the analog pin that you have chosen – in this case it is the analog pin A0, where we have the center pin of the potentiometer connected. The voltage at pin A0 will be mapped to a number between 0 and 1023, and this value will be assigned to the variable sensorValue.

If you recall from above, the actual voltage at pin A0 will be between 0 and 5 volts, depending on where your potentiometer is adjusted – this value gets mapped to the range 0 – 1023 with the help of the analog-to-digital converter. So we have a variable that has recorded the value at our potentiometer – what next? Well let's look at the value. To do that, we need to print it from the Arduino to our computer – and you guessed it, we will use the Serial library function println() to do just that…

```
Serial.println(sensorValue);
```

No big surprises here – we send as an argument the sensorValue variable to the function Serial.println() and our serial monitor window will display the resulting values.

To finish the sketch, we invoke the delay() function for one millisecond to make sure our next reading is a stable one and we start at the top of the loop() again. We record a new value using analogRead(), save it to the variable *sensorValue* and then print it to the computer.

All this is good and well, you might be thinking, but what does a potentiometer have to do with sensors? A potentiometer doesn't sense anything! You are right – but interestingly, many sensors work by applying the same principle that a potentiometer does – adjusting resistance. Take a photo-resister for example – it can be used to sense light – because the resistance changes based on the brightness of light that it is exposed to – this change in resistance will adjust the amount of voltage that a pin on the receiving end will receive. So now the ball is in your court – what can you use analogRead() for?

TRY ON YOUR OWN CHALLENGE:

- Change the analog pin to A2. Make adjustments in the code and the circuit.

- Try a different potentiometer in the circuit, does it affect the range of values displayed?

FURTHER READING:

Go to the Arduino Reference webpage and read the documentation on these functions.

https://www.arduino.cc/reference/en/

- analogRead()

SUPPLEMENTAL VIDEO LESSONS:

View these on the Programming Electronics Academy training portal.

- Using analogRead()

Reading Analog Pins and Converting the Input Value to a Voltage Range

KEY POINTS:

1 Transforming input from one range to another range is a common task. To do this we use a conversion factor.

2 A potentiometer is a voltage divider. In this circuit we use it to adjust the voltage between the 5 volt pin on the Arduino and A0.

3 The *float* data type is used for numbers with decimal points. Floats take up a lot of memory space, so use them only when precision is necessary.

In the last lesson you learned about using the analogRead() function to collect data from a sensor connected to one of the Arduino analog pins. The range of data we received from the analogRead() function was mapped between 0 to 1023.

What if we want to know the actual voltage being applied at the pin?

YOU WILL NEED:

1 Potentiometer (1) - Any resistance range will work.

2 Jumper wires (3)

3 Persian rug (1)

STEP-BY-STEP INSTRUCTIONS:

1 Place the potentiometer into your breadboard.

2 Run a jumper wire from the 5-Volt pin of the Arduino to either one of the outside pins of the potentiometer.

3 Run another jumper wire from one of the ground pins on the Arduino (labeled GND) to the other outside pin of the potentiometer.

4 Run the final jumper wire from pin A0 on the Arduino to the middle pin of the potentiometer.

5 Plug the Arduino into your computer.

6 Open up the Arduino IDE.

7 Open the sketch for this section.

8 Click the Verify button (check mark icon). The Arduino IDE will check your code for errors.

9 Click the Upload button (right arrow icon). You will see the TX and RX LEDs on your Arduino board begin to flash rapidly.

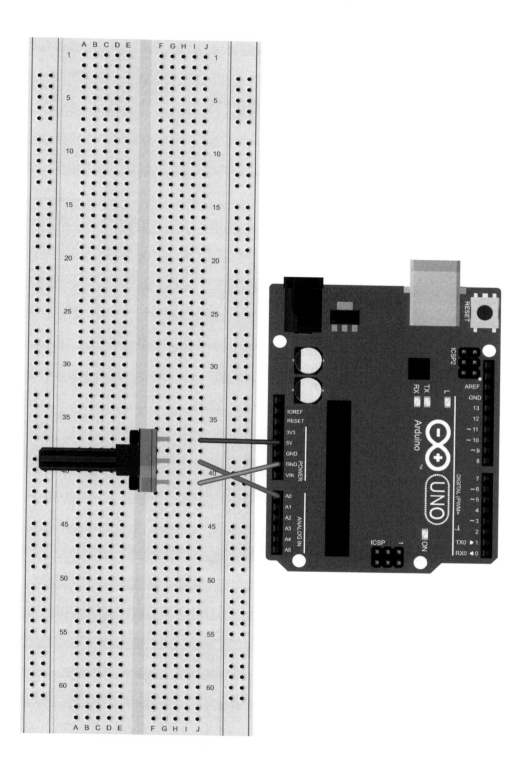

10 On the menu bar, go to Tools > Serial Monitor – this will open the Serial Monitor window – you should see numbers rolling down this screen.

11 Now adjust the knob of your potentiometer and watch the serial monitor window, the numbers should adjust between 0 and 5.

THE ARDUINO CODE

```
/*
 * ReadAnalogVoltage
 * Reads an analog input on pin 0, converts it to voltage,
 * and prints the result to the serial monitor.
 * Attach the center pin of a potentiometer to pin A0,
 * and the outside pins to +5V and ground.
 *
 * This example code is in the public domain.
*/



// The setup routine runs once when you press reset:
void setup() {
    // Initialize serial communication at 9600 bits per second:
    Serial.begin(9600);
}



// The loop routine runs over and over again forever:
void loop() {
    // Read the input on analog pin 0:
    int sensorValue = analogRead(A0);
```

```
// Convert the analog reading (which goes from 0 - 1023)
// to a voltage (0 - 5V):
float voltage = sensorValue * (5.0 / 1023.0);
// Print out the value you read:
Serial.println(voltage);
}
```

DISCUSS THE SKETCH:

This sketch does the exact same thing as the last lesson sketch except for one important change. It takes the reading provided by the analogRead() function and converts it into the actual voltage value at the respective analog pin. Let's start from the top to review what is taking place.

We have no variables to declare and initialize at the beginning of the sketch so we jump right into the setup() function. Inside the curly braces of setup() we begin serial communications by setting the baud rate. This is done using the function Serial.begin(9600).

```
void setup() {
    // Initialize serial communication at 9600 bits per second:
    Serial.begin(9600);
}
```

That is all there is to the setup() of this sketch. The next block of code is loop(). Inside the curly braces of loop() the first thing we do is read the value at analog pin A0 and assign it to an integer variable called *sensorValue*.

```
int sensorValue = analogRead(A0);
```

Once we have recorded this value, we want to convert it to an actual voltage. You will recall that the range returned by the analogRead() function is between 0 and 1023. We want this to reflect the actual voltage at the pin – which is between 0 and 5 volts depending on where the potentiometer knob is turned. So let's take a look at how we might accomplish this...

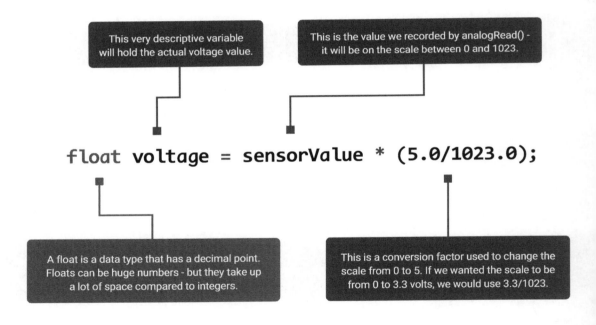

This very descriptive variable will hold the actual voltage value.

This is the value we recorded by analogRead() - it will be on the scale between 0 and 1023.

```
float voltage = sensorValue * (5.0/1023.0);
```

A float is a data type that has a decimal point. Floats can be huge numbers - but they take up a lot of space compared to integers.

This is a conversion factor used to change the scale from 0 to 5. If we wanted the scale to be from 0 to 3.3 volts, we would use 3.3/1023.

```
float voltage = sensorValue * (5.0 / 1023.0);
```

The first thing we encounter is a new data type – called *float*. A float is simply a number with a decimal point; say for example 3.14 or 2.17781778. Floats, also called *floating point numbers*, can be huge in value, and take much more time for the Arduino to churn through than integers – this is why they are used only when necessary.

We want the *voltage* variable set as a float data type because it will provide more resolution than an integer.

The *voltage* variable is set equal to a somewhat confusing calculation. Our goal is to take the value that analogRead() returns and convert it into an actual voltage value. We use a conversion factor to accomplish this feat. By multiplying *sensorValue* by (5.0/1023.0) it scales down the range from 0-1023 (which is the range that analogRead() returns) to the range 0-5 which is the actual range of the voltage. You can think of the conversion calculation by saying "*sensorValue* is to X volts as 5 volts is to 1023", where X is the converted voltage value we are trying to determine.

Once we have this new value, it is assigned to the variable *voltage* - all of this on one line of code.

Let's recap the program…

1 Read the sensor value at an analog pin.

2 Assign this value to a variable.

3 Convert this value to a voltage

4 Save the voltage measurement to another variable

5 And then…

Well, we print it back to the serial monitor window so we can see what the voltage is at our pin.

The loop() will start over again, it will sample a new value at the pin, it will convert that value and print it, and loop and loop and loop – you get the idea.

TRY ON YOUR OWN CHALLENGE:

- Switch from using the 5-volt pin on the Arduino to the 3.3-volt pin. Make sure to adjust the conversion factor.

- Instead of converting to a voltage value, can you change the conversion factor to return a range from 0 to 100?

FURTHER READING:

Go to the Arduino Reference webpage and read the documentation on these functions.

https://www.arduino.cc/reference/en/

- float
- map()

SUPPLEMENTAL VIDEO LESSONS:

View these on the Programming Electronics Academy training portal.

- How to read analog voltages

Fade an LED with Pulse Width Modulation Using analogWrite()

KEY POINTS:

1 The "if statement" allows you to set a condition. If the condition is met, then a piece of code *will* run - if the condition is not met, then the code *will not* run.

2 analogWrite() is used to adjust the voltage at the digital pins incrementally - not just HIGH or LOW. This is done using Pulse Width Modulation.

3 analogWrite() has nothing to do with the analog pins.

4 If a pin is set as an OUTPUT with pinMode(), it can *source* voltage.

Let's expand the repertoire of output that we can use by looking at the function analogWrite().

I experienced much confusion with analogWrite(), because I suspected that it had to do with the analog pins on the Arduino. The function, however, has nothing to do with the analog pins.

There are 5 pins on most Arduino boards marked with 'PWM' next to the pin number (on some boards it is an "~" symbol) – these pins can be invoked to rapidly change the power being applied at the pin – this is a technique called *pulse width modulation* (PWM).

YOU WILL NEED:

1 LED (1) - Any color is fine.

2 220 ohm resistor (1)

3 Alligator clip (1)

4 Glacial ice cubes (4)

STEP-BY-STEP INSTRUCTIONS:

1 Take the short leg of the LED and insert it in the GND pin.

2 Take either leg of the resistor and place it in pin 9.

3 Connect the long leg of the LED with the other leg of the resistor using an alligator clip

4 Plug the Arduino into your computer with the USB cable

5 Open up the Arduino IDE

6 Open the sketch for this section.

7 Click the Verify button (check mark icon). The Arduino IDE will check your code for errors.

8 Click the Upload button (right arrow icon). You will see the TX and RX LEDs on your Arduino board begin to flash rapidly.

9 Watch in mesmerizing amazement as the LED fades in and out.

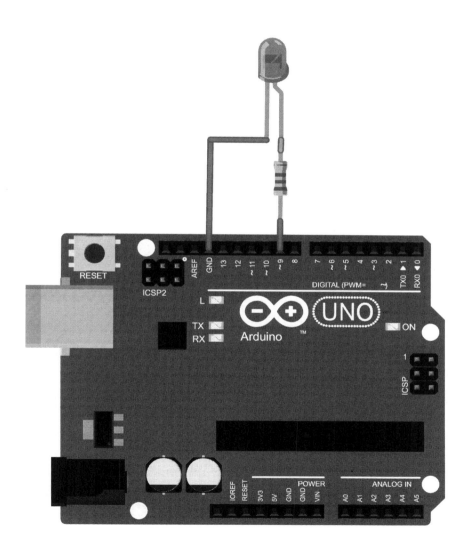

THE ARDUINO CODE:

```
/*
 * Fade
 * This example shows how to fade an LED on pin 9
 * using the analogWrite() function.
 *
 * This example code is in the public domain.
 */


int led = 9;          // The pin that the LED is attached to
int brightness = 0;   // How bright the LED is
int fadeAmount = 5;   // How many points to fade the LED by


// The setup routine runs once when you press reset:
void setup() {
    // Declare pin 9 to be an output:
    pinMode(led, OUTPUT);
}


// The loop routine runs over and over again forever:
void loop() {
    // Set the brightness of pin 9:
    analogWrite(led, brightness);

    // Change the brightness for next time through the loop:
    brightness = brightness + fadeAmount;
```

```
    // Reverse the direction of the fading at the ends of the fade:
    if (brightness == 0 || brightness == 255) {
        fadeAmount = -fadeAmount;
    }

    // Wait for 30 milliseconds to see the dimming effect
    delay(30);
}
```

DISCUSS THE SKETCH:

The sketch starts with the usual multi-line comment describing the program and how to set up the circuit. The first block of code we encounter is the declaration and initialization of three integer variables. Notice that the variable names are descriptive of their function – remember this when naming your variables! Names should help people understand the purpose of the code.

```
int led = 9;          // The pin that the LED is attached to
int brightness = 0;   // How bright the LED is
int fadeAmount = 5;   // How many points to fade the LED by
```

The *brightness* variable will store the value of the current brightness of the LED. *fadeAmount* is the rate at which the LED will fade and brighten. And of course, as the comments explain, *led* is simply the pin number where we have attached the LED (through a 220 ohm resistor).

Now that we have declared and initialized our variables, we move on to setting up the board with the setup() function...

```
void setup() {
    // Declare pin 9 to be an output:
    pinMode(led, OUTPUT);
}
```

The only thing we do here is set the mode of pin 9 as an OUTPUT using the pinMode() function. Recall that pinMode() takes two arguments – the pin number and the mode. In this case we assign the pin number using the variable *led*, which we previously initialized as the number 9. By now you know that setup() only runs once – the code inside the setup() curly bracket will only be executed a single time by the Arduino.

Where the real action happens is in loop().

The first function we encounter in the loop() is analogWrite(). This function invokes the *Pulse Width Modulation* capabilities of the Arduino board. Pulse Width Modulation basically adjusts the power output at the pin. So you can have a lot of power or a little power applied at the pin, it's your call, just tell the analogWrite() function which pin to modulate and how much power you want applied. The scale is from 0 to 255 with zero being the lowest power setting and 255 being the highest. For a discussion of what is actually happening with pulse width modulation check out the further reading section and the supplemental video lessons.

As alluded to above, analogWrite() takes two arguments...

```
analogWrite(pin, value);
```

You can utilize analogWrite() with pins 3, 5, 6, 9, 10 and 11 - recall there is a "PWM" or "~" next to the pin number on the board.

In this sketch we use the arguments:

```
analogWrite(led, brightness);
```

The first thing we do in the loop is write a value to pin 9 (recall that *led* holds the number 9) where we have our LED attached (through a resistor) – and we set the value to 0 (zero is what our brightness variable initially holds). This will keep our LED dark to start with.

KEY POINTS ABOUT THE analogWrite() FUNCTION

- Has to do with the analog pins
- Can be used with pins 3, 5, 6, 9, 10 and 11 on the Arduino UNO
- Uses Pulse Width Modulation (PWM) to adjust power output
- Takes two arguments
  - Pin Number
  - Value

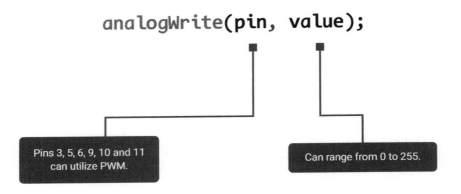

The next line of code we encounter is:

```
brightness = brightness + fadeAmount;        These are the values
   (0)     =    (0)     +    (5)     ←——————  the first time
                                              through the loop
```

We take the current value of *brightness* and add the *fadeAmount* to it, then we save this new value back to the brightness variable. Now the *brightness* variable holds the number 5.

You can see that we are increasing the brightness variable, this in turn will make the LED brighter. When we start the loop over and use analogWrite(led, brightness) – it will be 5 "levels" brighter than it was before. Every time through the loop we add 5 to our *brightness* variable until we have one very bright LED.

You see, however, that if this were to continue, the brightness variable will quickly go over the top range of 255 our analogWrite() limit – not to mention, it won't fade if the brightness variable only increases in value. We need a way to test the value of the brightness variable, and then change it when it gets to its limit.

Welcome *if statement*. The *if statement* is my favorite function – it can do so much and is so easy to use. An *if statement* checks a condition – if that condition is met, then it does something – if the condition is not met, then it does nothing. That easy.

Let's say you are picking apples. You have an *if statement* running in your brain – something like…

```
if (apple is ripe AND not rotten) {
    pick_apple()
    put_in_basket()
}
```

The condition is what you type inside the parenthesis after the word *if*. Inside the curly braces you type the code that you want to execute if the condition is met. If the condition is not met, the instructions are not executed – in the example above you would not want to pick unripened or rotten apples.

Let's take a look at how the if statement helps us to fade the LED.

```
if (brightness == 0 || brightness == 255) {
    fadeAmount = -fadeAmount;
}
```

The condition here looks a little confusing, but let's walk through it, and see if we can figure it out.

For starters the || lines mean OR in computer speak. This condition says "if the brightness variable equals zero OR if the brightness variable equals 255".

You probably noticed the fact that they use a double equal sign – weird eh? The double equal sign is a *comparison operator* that asks "are these two values equal?". The reason we need a double equal sign is because if we use a single equal sign, then we would be assigning a value to the *brightness* variable – and we do not want to assign anything – we want to compare! It is a subtle change in syntax but a huge change in application. There are several comparison operators that you will use. Further Reading at the end of this section has a link to more comparison operators.

```
brightness = 0
// This statement assigns a value to the brightness variable
brightness == 0
// This statement compares the brightness variable with 0
```

The condition in an *if statement* will be either true or false. If the condition is true, than the code enclosed in the curly brackets will execute.

Let's say that our *brightness* variable is all the way up to the value 255.

```
if (brightness == 0 || brightness == 255) {
    fadeAmount = -fadeAmount;
    // Applying a negative sign to the variable
    // will change its sign from positive to negative
}
```

This condition is met – now what?

All we do is a sneaky change of sign.

```
fadeAmount = -fadeAmount;
// Applying a negative sign to the variable
// will change its sign from positive to negative
```

By assigning the *fadeAmount* variable to a negative version of itself, we are able to change its sign from positive to negative. The *fadeAmount* was being used to increase the value of the *brightness* variable - now that it is negative, each time through the loop() we will subtract 5 from the *brightness* variable – and the LED will start to dim because the value we write with analogWrite() is decreasing.

The best part about this clever line of code is that once the *brightness* variable decreases to zero, it will switch *fadeAmount* to positive and start the whole process over again! A fading LED – and easy to do!

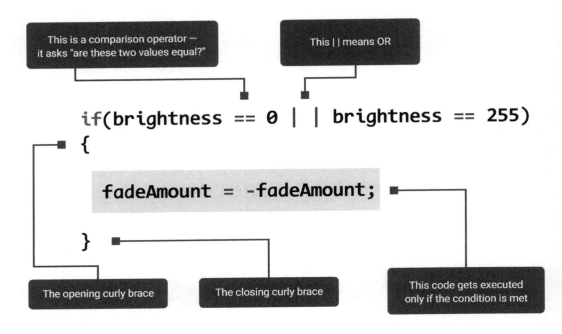

The final step is slowing down the fading process. We use the delay() function to make sure we get to see the fading.

```
// Wait for 30 milliseconds to see the dimming effect
delay(30);
```

There is an interesting aspect of human vision called *persistence of vision*. Basically, if something flashes very rapidly – then we don't perceive it as flashing, we perceive it as a steady image. Since our microcontroller operates rapidly, all this fading and brightening would not be noticeable if we didn't slow it down with a delay.

Once we get to the end of the sketch we start back at the top of the loop(). We write the power level to the LED, we increment *brightness*, we check if *brightness* is maximized or minimized and then if necessary make the appropriate change to the sign of the *fadeAmount* variable.

TRY ON YOUR OWN CHALLENGE:

- At the top of the sketch, where the variable *fadeAmount* is declared and initialized, change the value and see what happens.

- What happens if you reduce the delay time?

- Can you fade multiple LEDs at the same time? (Hint: you will have to add another variable and use the analogWrite() function twice instead of once)

FURTHER READING:

Go to the Arduino Reference webpage and read the documentation on these functions.

https://www.arduino.cc/reference/en/

- analogWrite()
- if statement
- Comparison Operators
- Boolean Operators

SUPPLEMENTAL VIDEO LESSONS

View these on the Programming Electronics Academy training portal.

- A Simple Example of Using PWM With Arduino

CHAPTER

03

CONTROL

This is where things start getting interesting. The following chapter introduces the fundamental control functions that are present in nearly every programming language in the known universe. If you master this chapter, you will be paid back in tenfold when the time arrives to solve a programming challenge.

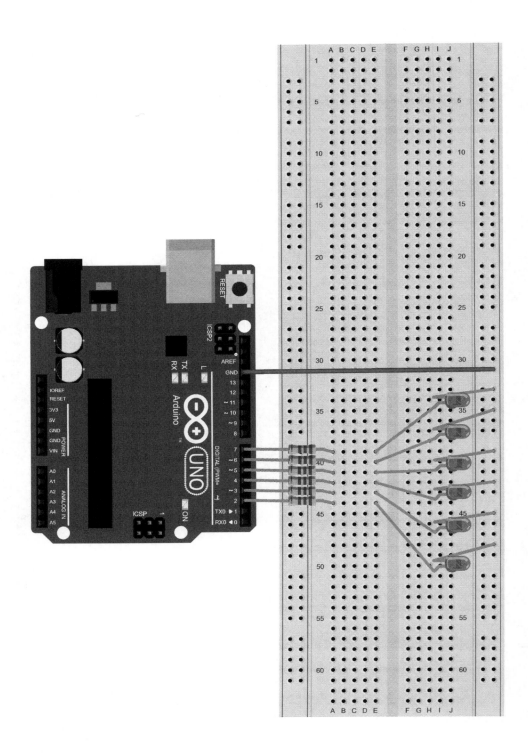

If-Else Statement, Comparison Operators and Conditions

KEY POINTS:

1   *if-else statements* give programmers several options for setting conditions. If the first condition is not met, the program will check the next condition.

2   Comparison operators are our friends from elementary school, they include greater than >, less than >, equal to ==, and some other operators you are sure to recognize.

3   A *qualifier* changes the properties of a variable.

4   A variable with the qualifier *const* in front of its declaration is a constant variable. These variables cannot be changed anywhere in the sketch once they have been declared.

In the last lesson we learned about the *if statement*. The *if statement* was the perfect choice for setting up instructions to run only when certain conditions were met. "If 30 seconds has passed – stop the heating element" or "If the sensor perceives a wall – turn 180 Degrees".

This lesson will expand on this amazingly useful function and show you how to stack different conditions to satisfy the flexibility you want in your designs.

YOU WILL NEED:

1. Potentiometer (1) - Doesn't matter what resistance range.

2. 220 ohm resistor (1)

3. LED (1) - Any color will do.

4. Jumper wires (3)

5. Alligator clip (1)

6. Dull machete with wood handle (1)

STEP-BY-STEP INSTRUCTIONS:

1. Place the potentiometer in the breadboard.

2. Place a jumper wire from one of the outside leads of the potentiometer to the 5V pin on Arduino.

3. Place a jumper wire from the other outside lead of the potentiometer to one of the GND pins.

4. Place the final jumper wire from the center pin of the potentiometer to the A0 pin.

5. Connect either side of the 220 ohm resistor to pin 13.

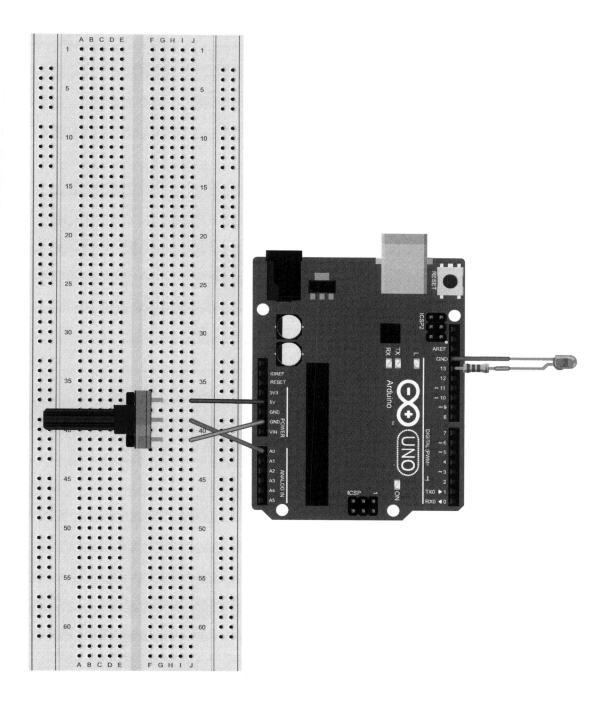

---

6 Connect the short leg of the LED to GND (the GND pin next to pin 13 is the most convenient).

7 Attach the other leg of the resistor to the long leg of the LED.

8 Plug your Arduino into your computer with the USB cable.

9 Open the Arduino IDE.

10 Open the sketch for this section.

11 Click the Verify button (check mark icon). The Arduino IDE will check your code for errors.

12 C Click the Upload button (right arrow icon). You will see the TX and RX LEDs on your Arduino board begin to flash rapidly.

13 Open up the Serial Monitor window. Tools > Serial Monitor.

14 Adjust the potentiometer and watch as the LED turns on and off based on the knob position.

THE ARDUINO CODE:

```
/*
 * Conditionals - If statement
 * This example demonstrates the use of if() statements.
 * It reads the state of a potentiometer (an analog input)
 * and turns on an LED only if the LED goes above a certain
 * threshold level. It prints the analog value regardless
 * of the level.
 *
 * The circuit:
 * - Potentiometer connected to analog pin 0.
```

```
* - Center pin of the potentiometer goes to the analog pin.
* - Side pins of the potentiometer go to +5V and ground
* - LED connected from digital pin 13 to ground
*
* Note:
* On most Arduino boards, there is already an LED on the board
* connected to pin 13, so you don't need any extra components
* for this example.
*
* This example code is in the public domain.
*/



// These constants won't change:
const int analogPin = A0;  // Pin that the sensor is attached to
const int ledPin = 13;     // Pin that the LED is attached to
const int threshold = 400; // An arbitrary threshold level
    // that's in the range of the analog input



void setup() {
    // Initialize the LED pin as an output:
    pinMode(ledPin, OUTPUT);
    // Initialize serial communications:
    Serial.begin(9600);
}



void loop() {
    // Read the value of the potentiometer:
    int analogValue = analogRead(analogPin);
```

```
    // If the analog value is high enough, turn on the LED:
    if (analogValue > threshold) {
        digitalWrite(ledPin, HIGH);
    } else {
        digitalWrite(ledPin,LOW);
    }

// Print the analog value:
Serial.println(analogValue);
delay(1);      // Delay in between reads for stability
}
```

DISCUSS THE SKETCH:

In this sketch we measure voltage at an analog pin from 0 to 1023 – this voltage changes based on where the knob of the potentiometer is set. We then define a threshold value somewhere in this range, let's pick the number 400. When the value measured at the analog pin is above 400, we turn on the LED at pin 13, when the voltage is below 400 we turn the LED off. It's as easy as that.

Make sure you read the sketch and try to figure out what is taking place before moving on.

This program might look long to you – the previous ones were a bit shorter. A good way to approach any program long or short is to cut it up into chunks and only consider pieces of it at a time. The first chunk in this sketch is the multi-line comments that clearly describe:

1 What the program will do

2 How to set up the circuit and the components you will need

3 Any pertinent notes

4 The license the program is released under (if any)

This might seem like a lot of stuff – but I would recommend you do the same thing for your programs! This information will not only help you understand what the heck you intended when you wrote the program but if you make the program available for others then your comments will help them as well.

Some of the functions that are now integrated into the Arduino IDE were created by people just like you – they had a problem, they found a solution with some well written code, they made it available to all the Arduino users in the world – and everybody else found it useful – and before you know it your code is famous and you win the Nobel peace prize.

Enough of this tirade, let's move onto the first block of code that will be executed by the Arduino.

```
const int analogPin = A0;  // Pin that the sensor is attached to
const int ledPin = 13;     // Pin that the LED is attached to
const int threshold = 400; // An arbitrary threshold level
   // that's in the range of the analog input
```

Notice that all the variables have *const* in front of them. This keyword stands for *constant*. A constant is classified as a qualifier – it adjusts the behavior of the variable being declared. It is similar to an adjective in a sentence – "The squishy material," squishy qualifies how the material will behave.

It might seem counterintuitive to the whole point of variables, but the constant qualifier will stop the variable from changing through out your program. It protects the value from start to finish.

Why do this? It protects you from *unintentionally* writing a new value to the variable. It happens more often than you might think – I recommend using constants when the variable will not change in the program.

The integer constants we declare are pretty straightforward. The variables *analogPin* and *ledPin* are those pins the potentiometer and LED will be attached to on the Arduino board. *threshold* is the arbitrary number chosen as the condition to turn our LED on or off.

The next block of code is setup(). Here, we have to set the mode of a pin and set up serial communications.

```
void setup() {
    // Initialize the LED pin as an output:
    pinMode(ledPin, OUTPUT);
    // Initialize serial communications:
    Serial.begin(9600);
}
```

Recall that all pins are by default set to INPUT, so we do not have to explicitly set the pin mode for our analogPin A0 as an INPUT – though I would argue it is best to do so for clarity.

You should have serial communication down pat. We use the begin() function from the Serial library with a baud rate of 9600.

Now that we have things setup, let's get into the loop(). The first line of code we encounter reads from the value at the analog pin A0 and assigns this value to an integer variable called *analogValue*.

```
int analogValue = analogRead(analogPin);
```

To do this we use the analogRead() function. Recall that analogRead() will return a value between 0 and 1023. This value will change as we adjust the potentiometer. This line of code is checking the position of the potentiometer every time through the loop().

The next thing we want to do is compare the value we just read from the analog pin to our *threshold* value. The *if-else statement* is perfect for this.

```
if (analogValue > threshold) {
    digitalWrite(ledPin, HIGH);
} else {
    digitalWrite(ledPin,LOW);
}
```

You have seen the *if statement* before, now we add an *else statement*. The *if statement* checks a condition in the parenthesis, if it is true, then the code in the curly brackets is executed – if the condition is not met (false), then it moves to the *else statement*.

Consider this pseudo code:

```
if (apple is NOT rotten) {
    Put_Apple_In_Basket()
} else {
    Throw_Apple_At_Brother()
}
```

You can see that the *else statement* gives you control over what to do when the condition in the *if statement* is not met. In a later lesson we will talk about the *else-if statement* which will offer even further control over conditions.

If this is TRUE,

```
if (analogValue > threshold)
{
    digitalWrite(ledPin, HIGH);
}
else
{
    digitalWrite(ledPin, LOW);
}
```

Do this.

Otherwise, do this.

In this example the condition we are interested in is:

```
analogValue > threshold
```

If this is true we turn the LED on by using the digitalWrite() function:

```
if (analogValue > threshold) {
    digitalWrite(ledPin, HIGH);
}
```

If this condition is false we turn off the LED by executing the code inside the curly brackets of the *else statement*:

```
else {
    digitalWrite(ledPin,LOW);
}
```

Before we continue discussing the sketch, let's do a quick overview of *Comparison Operators*.

The condition set in an *if-else statement* will use what are called comparison operators. The list of comparison operators on the Arduino Reference page is as follows:

- == (equal to)

- != (not equal to)

- < (less than)

- > (greater than)

- <= (less than or equal to)

- >= (greater than or equal to)

These operators offer a broad spectrum of comparisons to use. It's vital to pay close attention to the syntax of the comparison operators. Accidentally dropping an equal sign, or typing a > instead of a < is easy to do, and usually leaves you scratching your head when the program acts differently than you might have expected.

Now that we have turned the LED on or off depending on the position of the potentiometer, let's see exactly what values are being read. We want to do this to ensure the program is doing what we think it should and also to make sure our potentiometer (sensor) is working properly.

```
// Print the analog value:
Serial.println(analogValue);
```

This line of code uses the println() function from the Serial library – which (as you know by now) sends the values from the Arduino to your computer. Adjust your potentiometer and watch the values change in the Serial Monitor window. Then adjust the potentiometer so the value is right at the 400 threshold and make sure the LED is responding appropriately.

Finally, we want to slow down the readings to add some stability. We do this with the delay() function.

```
delay(1);     // Delay in between reads for stability
```

Let's recap. First we read the value at the analog pin and assign that value to a variable. Next we check if that variable is more than or less than our threshold value. If it is above the threshold the LED turns on, if it is below the threshold the LED turns off.

We also want to see the actual values at the analog pin, so we print them to the serial monitor. Finally we wait a millisecond before our next reading – which starts the loop() at the top.

You can see how handy the *if-else statement* can be. As I have said previously, the *if-else statement* is a staple of programming – you will see it (or a similar form of it), in any programming language you encounter henceforth.

TRY ON YOUR OWN CHALLENGE:

● Adjust the value of the *threshold* variable.

● Write an additional *if statement* to turn on the LED when the *analogValue* variable is less than 100. The LED should turn on when *analogValue* is greater than 400 and less than 100.

SUPPLEMENTAL VIDEO LESSONS:

View these on the Programming Electronics Academy training portal.

- If Statement Application: Trigger an Action with a Button Press

For Loop Iteration

KEY POINTS:

1 The *for loop* allows you to run a piece of code over and over again while incrementing a variable to count the number of iterations - once a condition is met, the *for loop* will stop.

2 *for loops* allow a programmer to do in a very few lines of code what would otherwise require pages of code.

There are few functions so useful that you find them everywhere. The *for loop* is one of those functions.

A *for loop* repeats an action for a specified number of iterations, reducing the lines of code that need to be written thus making the programmer's life easier.

In this example we are setting out to make a row of LEDs light up somewhat similar to Kit in Knight Rider.

YOU WILL NEED:

1. LED (6)

2. 220 ohm resistor (6)

3. Jumper wire (1)

4. Red canary (42)

STEP-BY-STEP INSTRUCTIONS:

1. Connect one side of a resistor into pin 2, connect the other side into a row on the breadboard.

2. Connect the long leg of the LED to the row in the breadboard where you attached the resistor.

3. Connect the short leg of the LED to one of the power strip columns on your breadboard.

4. Now connect a resistor to pin 3, and put the other leg in a row on the breadboard (a different one then your first LED).

5. Connect an LED in the same manner – make sure the short leg goes in the SAME power strip column as the previous LED.

6. Add LEDs and resistors in this fashion through pin 7.

7. Using a jumper wire, connect the common power strip to a GND pin on the Arduino.

8. Connect the Arduino to your computer.

9. Open up the Arduino IDE.

10. Open the sketch for this section.

11. Click the Verify button (check mark icon). The Arduino IDE will check your code for errors.

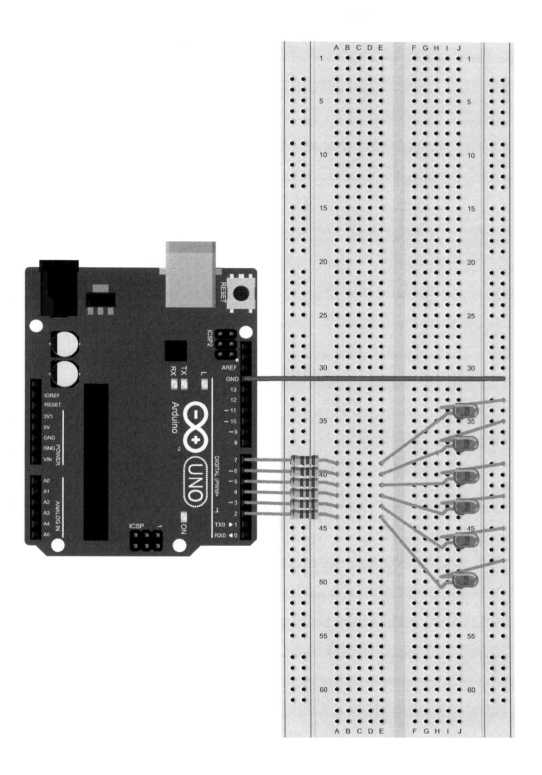

12 Click the Upload button (right arrow icon). You will see the TX and RX LEDs on your Arduino board begin to flash rapidly.

13 Watch in awe as your LEDs turn on and off in sequence.

THE ARDUINO CODE

```
/*
 * For Loop Iteration
 * Demonstrates the use of a for() loop.
 * Lights multiple LEDs in sequence, then in reverse.
 *
 * The circuit:
 * - LEDs from pins 2 through 7 to ground
 *
 * This example code is in the public domain.
 */



int timer = 100; // The higher the number, the slower the timing.

void setup() {
    // Use a for loop to initialize each pin as an output:
    for (int thisPin = 2; thisPin < 8; thisPin++) {
        pinMode(thisPin, OUTPUT);
    }
}
```

```
void loop() {
    // Loop from the lowest pin to the highest:
    for (int thisPin = 2; thisPin < 8; thisPin++) {
        // Turn the pin on:
        digitalWrite(thisPin, HIGH);
        delay(timer);
        // Turn the pin off:
        digitalWrite(thisPin, LOW);
    }

    // Loop from the highest pin to the lowest:
    for (int thisPin = 7; thisPin >= 2; thisPin--) {
        // Turn the pin on:
        digitalWrite(thisPin, HIGH);
        delay(timer);
        // Turn the pin off:
        digitalWrite(thisPin, LOW);
    }
}
```

DISCUSS THE SKETCH:

The first executable code we find in the sketch is the declaration of the *timer* variable…

```
int timer = 100; // The higher the number, the slower the timing.
```

This integer variable (note the descriptive name) sets the rate the LEDs turn on and off.

Our next friendly block of code is setup(). In this setup() function we run into our first *for loop*:

```
void setup() {
    for (int thisPin = 2; thisPin < 8; thisPin++) {
        pinMode(thisPin, OUTPUT);
    }
}
```

Let's take a close look at what is inside the parenthesis following the *for loop*:

```
for (int thisPin = 2; thisPin < 8; thisPin++)
```

There are three separate statements in the parenthesis separated by a semicolon. The first statement is initialization of the counter variable used in the *for loop*, it looks like any other variable declaration and initialization you have seen:

```
int thisPin = 2;
```

The *thisPin* variable is what is used in the next statement – called the *condition*:

```
thisPin < 8;
```

This is the test condition that tells the loop to keep going or to stop. If the condition is TRUE, the code in the curly brackets of the *for loop* will be executed again, if the condition is FALSE, the program will stop executing the statement in the *for loop* and move forward in the program.

When we first evaluate this test condition, the *thisPin* variable equals 2 and the test is…

$2 < 8$

We know that 2 is less than 8, so we execute the code in the curly brackets of the *for loop*. But before we look at the code in the curly brackets of the *for loop* let's finish with the final statement in the parenthesis of the *for loop*:

```
thisPin++
```

The "++" syntax means the same thing as "Add 1 to the value of variable *thisPin*". Since "adding the number one" to a value is such a common calculation to perform, the syntax '++' was created to make it even easier. Otherwise you would write:

```
thisPin = thisPin + 1 // Which is the same as thisPin++
```

On an aside, there is also a shorthand for decrementing a variable by 1:

```
thisPin-- // This shorthand subtracts the value 1 from thisPin
```

On yet another aside, you can increment and decrement by *any amount* using the following shorthand:

```
thisPin += 42
// The += means "add 42 to the variable on the left"
// a handy syntax shortcut

thisPin -= 42
// The -= means "subtract 42 to the variable on the left"
// another handy syntax shortcut
```

In most cases *for loops* increment by the number 1, just keep in mind that you can increment however you choose.

Enough about incrementing! Ok, here is the deal…if the condition of the *for loop* is met, then the code in the curly brackets gets executed *and then* the counter variable is incremented. The condition is then checked again - if it is still true, then the code in the curly brackets is once again executed and then the counter variable is incremented (again). Eventually, as the counter variable changes, the condition will no longer be satisfied and the for loop will end (though if your condition is never met, the for loop will go on forever!)

```
for (int thisPin = 2; thisPin < 8; thisPin++) {
    pinMode(thisPin, OUTPUT);
}
```

In this example, when the *thisPin* variable gets larger than 7, the loop will stop.

What is awesome about the counter variable is that we usually use it inside the *for loop* to help do something. In this case, the code that gets executed is:

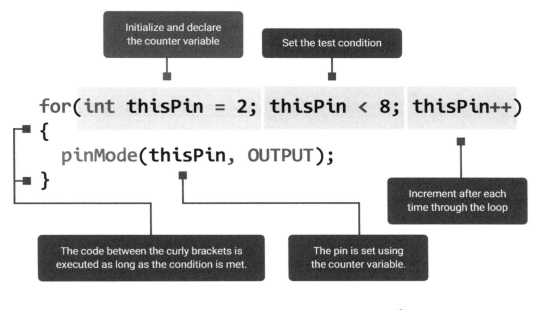

CHAPTER 3 - CONTROL

```
pinMode(thisPin, OUTPUT);
```

You are familiar with the pinMode() function – it sets the mode of a pin. Here the number of the pin is specified by the counter variable. So what happens? The first time through the *for loop*, the *thisPin* variable is equal to 2. Since 2 is less than 8 (the test condition), we go ahead and execute the code inside the curly brackets:

```
pinMode(thisPin, OUTPUT);
         (2)              ◄──── Pin 2 is set as OUTPUT
```

After the *for loop* ends the first time, we increment *thisPin* (thisPin++) so it now holds the value 3.

Next we check the condition again, and since 3 is indeed less than 8, the code is executed another time:

```
pinMode(thisPin, OUTPUT);
         (3)              ◄──── Pin 3 is set as OUTPUT
```

After the *for loop* ends the second time, we increment *thisPin* as before so it now holds the value 4. We check the condition – we know 4 is less than 8, and we execute the code in the curly brackets of the *for loop* again:

```
pinMode(thisPin, OUTPUT);
        (4)                         ◄──────  Pin 4 is set as OUTPUT
```

This incrementing and condition testing goes on until *thisPin* is equal to 8, now the test condition is not met, and the *for loop* ends – and all of our pins have their mode set.

Seems a bit convoluted perhaps? Consider a *for loop* vs. what "hard coding" would require:

```
pinMode(2, OUTPUT);
pinMode(3, OUTPUT);
pinMode(4, OUTPUT);
pinMode(5, OUTPUT);
pinMode(6, OUTPUT);
pinMode(7, OUTPUT);
```

You can see that the *for loop* saved us a lot of typing! With a *for loop* if you decide to add LEDs, all you have to do is change the test condition by simply changing a single number. In the hard coding version you have to add more pinMode() functions to get the same result. Efficiency rocks – stay away from hard coding.

That is a *for loop* in all its glory. How else can we use *for loops*?

The next block of code we encounter is the loop() function - notice that the loop() function is like an infinite *for loop*. In the body of our program we encounter our next *for loop*:

```
for (int thisPin = 2; thisPin < 8; thisPin++) {
    digitalWrite(thisPin, HIGH);  // Turn the pin on:
    delay(timer);
    digitalWrite(thisPin, LOW);   // Turn the pin off:
}
```

We see that all the code *in the parenthesis* following the *for loop* is identical to the previous example. What changes is the code that is executed. First we use the digitalWrite() function to light up the LED. Recall that digitalWrite() takes two arguments – the pin number and the type of output, either HIGH or LOW.

```
digitalWrite(thisPin, HIGH);
```

Here we apply HIGH voltage and the LED turns on. But which LED? The one specified by the counter variable, *thisPin*. Yes that's right, the number 2.

Let's enjoy the bright light for a little bit – the delay() function is handy for this. We delay the length of the *timer* variable which we set at the beginning of the sketch to the value 100:

```
delay(timer);
```

We pause 100 milliseconds and move to the next command:

```
digitalWrite(thisPin, LOW);
```

Now write LOW voltage to pin 2, and the LED will turn off.

What do you suspect happens now? Well, our counter variable is incremented and tested again – it will meet the condition, and the same thing will happen again, except now the specified pin will be number 3. This will continue all the way down to pin 7, at which point the condition will not be met and this *for loop* will end.

But don't despair, we have another *for loop*! We are going to reverse the order we blink the LEDs.

```
for (int thisPin = 7; thisPin >= 2; thisPin--) {
    // Turn the pin on:
    digitalWrite(thisPin, HIGH);
    delay(timer);
    // Turn the pin off:
    digitalWrite(thisPin, LOW);
}
```

Note that we have changed some things in the parenthesis. We initialize the *thisPin* variable at 7. Our test condition is now "is *thisPin* greater than or equal to 2?". Finally, our decrementing subtracts 1 from the value of *thisPin* every time through the *for loop*. Now we work backwards down the row, from pin 7 to pin 2, at which point the test condition is not met and this *for loop* ends.

And then we start back at the top of loop() and repeat it all over. The poor life of a microcontroller – gets a little monotonous I'm afraid. Keep in mind that every time a *for loop* starts again, it re-declares and re-initializes the counter variable to the value you specify.

This is a good time to start researching variable *scope*. The scope of a variable refers to where the variable can be used within a program. The variables that we declare at the top of the program, before setup() and loop(), have *global scope* – they can be used anywhere in the program. But the variables declared in the parenthesis of a *for loop*, can only be used inside that *for loop*.

More discussion on variable scope can be found in the supplemental video lessons at Programming Electronics Academy.

TRY ON YOUR OWN CHALLENGE:

- Adjust the value of the *timer* variable.

- Add additional LEDs at pin 8 and 9. Adjust all three *for loop* statements accordingly.

FURTHER READING:

Go to the Arduino Reference webpage and read the documentation on these functions.

https://www.arduino.cc/reference/en/

- for
- ++ and - -
- += and -=

SUPPLEMENTAL VIDEO LESSONS

View these on the Programming Electronics Academy training portal.

- Introduction to the For Loop
- Variable Scope

Using Arrays

KEY POINTS:

1 An *array* is a data type that can store lists if information.

2 An *array* is *zero indexed* meaning that the first item stored in an array is referred to by the number zero.

3 *for loops* and *arrays* are like inseparable friends, you almost always find one with the other.

Back in the old days, before medical information went digital – there were paper medical records. These were packets of information about when you were born, any conditions you have had, and maybe a picture of the tape worm they pulled out of your belly in high school. The purpose of the record was to organize information about your medical history in a way that allowed a healthcare practitioner to easily find and review your case.

Computer programs can organize information in a similar way. These records are called data structures – they are organized ways of storing data. One immensely handy data structure is the *array*. Arrays rock because they are easily created and indexed.

Indexing is how you find the information in your data structure. With the medical record example, it might be that all your immunizations are listed on page 5. No matter what patient record you review, you know page 5 will provide their immunization data.

An array has multiple elements – which would be the equivalent of pages in a medical record. The first page starts at zero.

If it seems strange to start the count at zero, don't worry, you are not alone. It is weird at first, but highly useful as you will discover. This is called *zero indexed*. That means if you have 5 elements in your array, the 5th element would be indexed with a 4.

Arrays can hold any thing you want as long as the contents are the same data type. When you declare an array, you say what the array will hold. For example:

```
int myArray[]; // This array will hold integers
dogs myArray[]; // This array will hold dogs
```

To initialize an array (put stuff in it), all you have to do is the following:

```
myArray[] = {spot, pluto, clifford, ruff};
```

You can declare and initialize at the same time:

```
dogs myArray[] = {spot, pluto, clifford, ruff};
```

If you want, you can specify the number of elements in your array when you declare it:

```
dogs myArray[4] = {spot, pluto, clifford, ruff};
```

If you put more elements in the declaration than you use to initialize, empty spaces are added to the end of the array and you can add things later:

```
dogs myArray[42] = {spot, pluto, clifford, ruff};
```

In this statement, the array is big enough to hold 42 dogs, but you only put in 4 to begin with, so you have 38 more dogs you could add later.

So how do I reference that 4th dog? What if someone asked you, "Monsieur, what is the name of the fourth dog in your array?" – I get that question a ton. You would respond:

```
myArray[3]; // This refers to the 4th element in the array
```

Remember that arrays are ZERO indexed. In this example:

```
dogs myArray[4] = {spot, pluto, clifford, ruff};
```

myArray[0] equals spot

myArray[1] equals pluto

myArray[2] equals clifford

myArray[3] equals ruff

OK, that is the intro on arrays, let's move onto the code and circuit to get our feet wet.

NOTE: *arrays* and *for loops* are like sisters who always hang out – to best comprehend this section, make sure you understand *for loops* from the previous lesson.

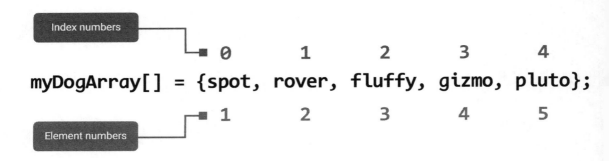

```
myDogArray[0]  ⟷  spot

myDogArray[1]  ⟷  rover

myDogArray[2]  ⟷  fluffy

myDogArray[3]  ⟷  gizmo

myDogArray[4]  ⟷  pluto
```

YOU WILL NEED:

1. LED (6)

2. 220 ohm resistor (6)

3. Jumper wire (1)

4. Dog leash (1)

STEP-BY-STEP INSTRUCTIONS:

If you did the previous tutorial this circuit exactly the same.

1. Connect one side of a resistor into pin 2, connect the other side into a row on the breadboard.

2. Connect the long leg of the LED to the row in the breadboard where you attached the resistor.

3. Connect the short leg of the LED to one of the power strip columns on your breadboard.

4. Now connect a resistor to pin 3, and put the other leg in a row on the breadboard (a different one then your first LED).

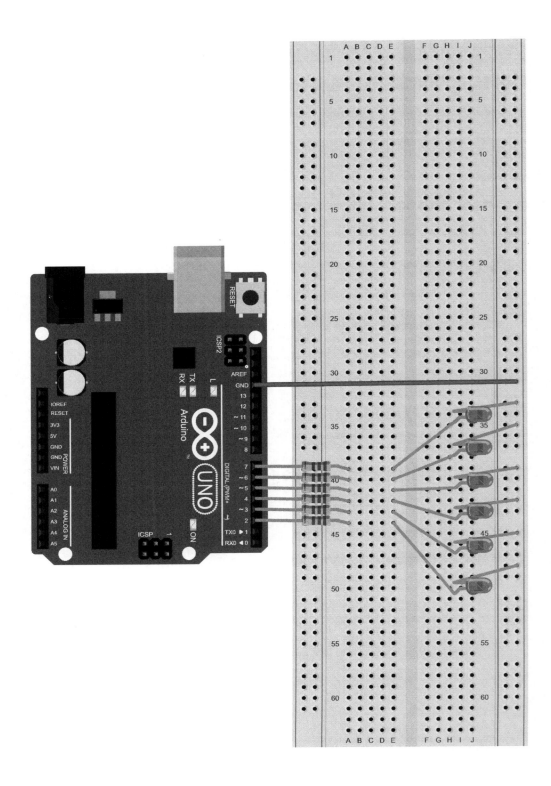

5 Connect an LED in the same manner – make sure the short leg goes in the SAME power strip column as the previous LED.

6 Add LEDs and resistors in this fashion through pin 7.

7 Using a jumper wire, connect the common power strip to a GND pin on the Arduino.

8 Connect the Arduino to your computer.

9 Open up the Arduino IDE.

10 Open the sketch for this section.

11 Click the Verify button (check mark icon). The Arduino IDE will check your code for errors.

12 Click the Upload button (right arrow icon). You will see the TX and RX LEDs on your Arduino board begin to flash rapidly.

13 Watch in awe as your LEDs turn on and off in a mixed sequence.

THE ARDUINO CODE

```
/*
 * Arrays
 * Demonstrates the use of an array to hold pin numbers
 * in order to iterate over the pins in a sequence.
 * Lights multiple LEDs in sequence, then in reverse.
 * Unlike the For Loop tutorial, where the pins have to be
 * contiguous, here the pins can be in any random order.
 *
```

```
 * The circuit:
 * - LEDs from pins 2 through 7 to ground
 *
 * This example code is in the public domain.
 */



int timer = 100;
    // The higher the number, the slower the timing.
int ledPins[] = {2, 7, 4, 6, 5, 3 };
    // An array of pin numbers to which LEDs are attached
int pinCount = 6;
    // The number of pins (i.e. the length of the array)



void setup() {
    // The array elements are numbered from 0 to (pinCount - 1).
    // Use a for loop to initialize each pin as an output:
    for (int thisPin = 0; thisPin < pinCount; thisPin++) {
        pinMode(ledPins[thisPin], OUTPUT);
    }
}



void loop() {
    // Loop from the lowest pin to the highest:
    for (int thisPin = 0; thisPin < pinCount; thisPin++) {
        // Turn the pin on:
        digitalWrite(ledPins[thisPin], HIGH);
        delay(timer);
```

```
    // Turn the pin off:
    digitalWrite(ledPins[thisPin], LOW);
  }


  // Loop from the highest pin to the lowest:
  for (int thisPin = pinCount - 1; thisPin >= 0;
  thisPin--) {
    // Turn the pin on:
    digitalWrite(ledPins[thisPin], HIGH);
    delay(timer);
    // Turn the pin off:
    digitalWrite(ledPins[thisPin], LOW);
  }
}
```

DISCUSS THE SKETCH:

This first piece of executable code is the declaration and initialization of variables:

```
int timer = 100;
    // The higher the number, the slower the timing.
int ledPins[] = {2, 7, 4, 6, 5, 3 };
    // An array of pin numbers to which LEDs are attached
int pinCount = 6;
    // The number of pins (i.e. the length of the array)
```

You should be very familiar with how to declare and initialize integer variables by now, but let's take a look at the array that is being made:

```
int ledPins[] = {2, 7, 4, 6, 5, 3 };
   // An array of pin numbers to which LEDs are attached
```

This is an array that will hold integers, as the preceding *int* tells us. Keep in mind that the elements in this array represent pins where LEDs are attached. We have left the square brackets following the name of the array empty – this means the compiler (the program integrated with the Arduino IDE that turns our human readable code into machine readable code), will count the elements in the array and set its size – in this case it as an array of 6 elements (count them, I dare you!). The name of the array can be whatever you like; descriptive names are always good.

The next block of code is the setup() function. Here we assign pin modes using a combination of our array and a *for loop*:

```
void setup() {
    for (int thisPin = 0; thisPin < pinCount; thisPin++) {
        pinMode(ledPins[thisPin], OUTPUT);
    }
}
```

Ok, what's going on here? We have a *for loop*, the condition is:

```
thisPin < pinCount
```

We can see that *thisPin* is initialized at 0 and *pinCount* is equal to 6 (recall that *pinCount* was one of the variables we declared at the top). Every time through the *for loop*, *thisPin* is incremented by adding 1.

The code executed in the curly brackets makes use of our array and uses *thisPin* as the *index counter*. The function is our old friend pinMode() which takes two arguments 1) Which pin to set the mode and 2) What mode we set:

```
pinMode(ledPins[thisPin], OUTPUT);
```

To determine the outcome of this line of code recall that the value of *thisPin* was set to zero. So what does ledPins[0] refer to?

Let's look back…

```
int ledPins[] = { 2, 7, 4, 6, 5, 3 };
                   0, 1, 2, 3, 4, 5          Index of each element
```

Since zero indexes the first element of the array, it appears that pin 2 will be the first pin to get its mode set to an OUTPUT. The next time through the *for loop*, the variable *thisPin* will equal 1 (since it is incremented each time through the *for loop*). What will *ledPins*[1] refer to? Pin 7, since pin 7 is the second element in the array.

All the pins will get their mode set to OUTPUTs in this manner. Once *thisPin* is greater than 5, the *for loop* will stop. So now you have gotten a taste of using a *for loop* and an array together. The counter variable of the *for loop* acts as the indexing number for the array. As the counter variable is incremented, we reference the array element by element. We will have another chance to see this union in the loop().

The first block of code in loop() is:

```
for (int thisPin = 0; thisPin < pinCount; thisPin++) {
    // Turn the pin on:
    digitalWrite(ledPins[thisPin], HIGH);
    delay(timer);
    // Turn the pin off:
    digitalWrite(ledPins[thisPin], LOW);
}
```

Imagine that - another *for loop* and another array! Let's see what this one does...

We have the exact same statements in the *for loop* as before – we set *thisPin* equal to 0, the condition is *thisPin* < *pinCount*, and we increment *thisPin* by 1 each time through the *for loop*:

```
for (int thisPin = 0; thisPin < pinCount; thisPin++)
```

The code inside the *for loop* curly brackets will turn the LEDs on and off. To do this we use the digitalWrite() function. Recall digitalWrite() takes two arguments 1) it wants to know which pin and 2) whether you want HIGH or LOW voltage applied. We tell the function which pin by using an array:

```
digitalWrite(ledPins[thisPin], HIGH);
```

The first time through the *for loop*, the array will index as:

```
ledPins[0]
```

This is the first element in the array which is the number 2. Now the LED at pin 2 will turn on because we are applying 5 volts to that pin. If we fast forward to the next time we come to this function, *thisPin* will have been incremented, and the value of *thisPin* will be 1 as follows:

```
ledPins[1]
```

This will digitalWrite() to the second element in the array, which is 7. So our LED at pin 7 will turn on. But I am getting ahead of myself. First we have to enjoy the brightness, to do this we delay the program:

```
delay(timer);    // Nothing new here
```

Now we want to turn off the LED. The function is the exact same, we just write LOW voltage to the pin:

```
digitalWrite(ledPins[thisPin], LOW);
```

This continues through the *for loop* turning each LED referred to in the array on and off. Note that since the pin numbers in the array are not sequential, the LEDs "hop around" as they light up.

Now this would be well and good, but let's keep it interesting and start at the last element in the array and move to the first element – reversing the order the LEDs turn on and off.

```
for (int thisPin = pinCount - 1; thisPin >= 0; thisPin--) {
    // Turn the pin on:
    digitalWrite(ledPins[thisPin], HIGH);
```

```
  delay(timer);
  // Turn the pin off:
  digitalWrite(ledPins[thisPin], LOW);
}
```

Let's take a close look at the statements that setup the next *for loop*:

```
for (int thisPin = pinCount - 1; thisPin >= 0; thisPin--)
```

thisPin is now initialized to *pinCount*-1 (*pinCount* minus one). Keep in mind that *pinCount* was initialized to the value 6 at the beginning of our program. *pinCount* is the number of pins where LEDs are attached, and it is also the size of the array. But if we want to access the last element in the array, we need to start at *pinCount* minus one (because of our 0 index). This is peculiar at first, but after you write a couple *for loops* with arrays, it will be a snap.

Every time through the *for loop* we decrement the *thisPin* variable, thus working across the array from right to left. Let's take a look at the actual values as we work through the *for loop*:

As a reminder, this is what we stored in our array:

```
ledPins[] = {2, 7, 4, 6, 5, 3 };
          0, 1, 2, 3, 4, 5            Index of each element
```

```
// First time through
ledPins[5]      ←——————  this is the sixth element in the array,
                         which is the value 3


// Next time through the for loop —
// remember that thisPin is decremented...
ledPins[4]      ←——————  the 5th element in the array is 5


// Next time through the for loop
ledPins[3]      ←——————  the 4th element in the array is 6


// Next time through the for loop
ledPins[2]      ←——————  the 3rd element in the array is 4
```

I think you get the picture. When *thisPin* gets decremented to less than 0, than the *for loop* stops. In this way all the pins are turned on and off in reverse order. Once this is done we start at the top of the loop() and go at it again.

A final note about array indexing - let's say you put 3 elements in an array...

```
dogs poundArray[3] = {Spike, Scooby, Lassie};
```

...but then you try to get the 15th element in that array. You and I know there is no 15th element. We only put three elements in the array, if we try to index the 15th element:

```
poundArray[14]
```

The program doesn't like this...at all. And while it may compile correctly – it will not operate correctly. If your program starts acting all funky – or not acting at all – check your index and make sure you didn't index outside the size of the arrays.

TRY ON YOUR OWN CHALLENGE:

- Switch up the order of the values in the *ledPins*[] Array. Make sure you use the same values, just change the order.

- Add an additional LED at pin 8. Adjust the *ledPins*[] array and all three *for loop* statements accordingly.

FURTHER READING:

Go to the Arduino Reference webpage and read the documentation on these functions.

https://www.arduino.cc/reference/en/

- array

SUPPLEMENTAL VIDEO LESSONS

View these on the Programming Electronics Academy training portal.

Introduction to Arrays

Switch Case Statements

KEY POINTS:

1   *switch case* statements are useful when you want a list of options executed based on a variable value.

2   The *break* keyword is used in every *case* to exit from the *switch case* statement.

Here is a secret about human relations a boss from long ago once told me. If you and your spouse decide to go out to dinner do not ask "Where do you want to go?" instead give a list of options, "Do you want to go to Mike's Bar and Grill, The Dive, or La Pura Di Mona?"

This allows your spouse to make a quicker decision than having an endless list of local restaurants from which to choose.

We both know this doesn't work that great – but it works in programing pretty well – we call this method a *switch case* statement.

To get a *switch case* statement up and running you need to make a list of options. Your list might be something like:

case 0: Go to Nepal

case 1: Go to Norway

case 2: Go to Zanzibar

These options are referred to as *cases*. Here there are three cases. In order to switch from one case to another we use a variable that matches the case. So if we want to go to Norway, we need a variable of '1', if we want to change our destination to Zanzibar, we need our variable to change to '2'.

The syntax of a *switch case* statement is surprisingly simple:

```
switch (trip) {
    case 0:
        goTo(Nepal);
        break;
    case 1:
        goTo(Norway);
        break;
    case 2:
        goTo(Zanzibar);
        break;
}
```

It starts with the word switch(). Then in the parenthesis you type the name of the variable that determines the case. Here we have the variable *trip*. If *trip* = 0, then the lines of code following case 0: will get executed up to the point where the keyword *break* is found.

The *switch case* statement is trying to match a case with the variable in the parenthesis, it will skip over each case until it finds a match – if it does, the code in that case is executed. If no match between the variable and the cases is found, the *switch case* statement is ignored until the next time through the loop(), when it checks for a match again.

YOU WILL NEED:

1. Potentiometer (1) - Any resistance range will work.
2. Jumper wires (3)
3. Famous Tolstoy novel (1)

STEP-BY-STEP INSTRUCTIONS:

1. Place the potentiometer into the breadboard.
2. Run a jumper wire from the 5-Volt pin of the Arduino to either one of the outside pins of the potentiometer.
3. Run another jumper wire from one of the ground pins on the Arduino (labeled GND) to the other outside pin of the potentiometer.
4. Run the final jumper wire from pin A0 on the Arduino to the middle pin of the potentiometer.
5. Plug the Arduino into your computer.

6 Open up the Arduino IDE.

7 Open the sketch for this section.

8 Click the Verify button (check mark icon). The Arduino IDE will check your code for errors.

9 Click the Upload button (right arrow icon). You will see the TX and RX LEDs on your Arduino board begin to flash rapidly.

10 On the menu bar, go to Tools > Serial Monitor – this will open the Serial Monitor window – you should see numbers rolling down this screen.

11 Now adjust the knob of your potentiometer and watch the serial monitor window, the output changes based on the potentiometer adjustment.

THE ARDUINO CODE:

```
/*
 * Switch Case Statement
 * Demonstrates the use of a switch case statement. The switch case
 * statement allows you to choose from among a set of discrete
 * values of a variable. It's like a series of if statements.
 *
 * This example code is in the public domain.
 */



const int min = 0;      // Lowest reading at analog pin
const int max = 1023;   // Highest reading at analog pin
```

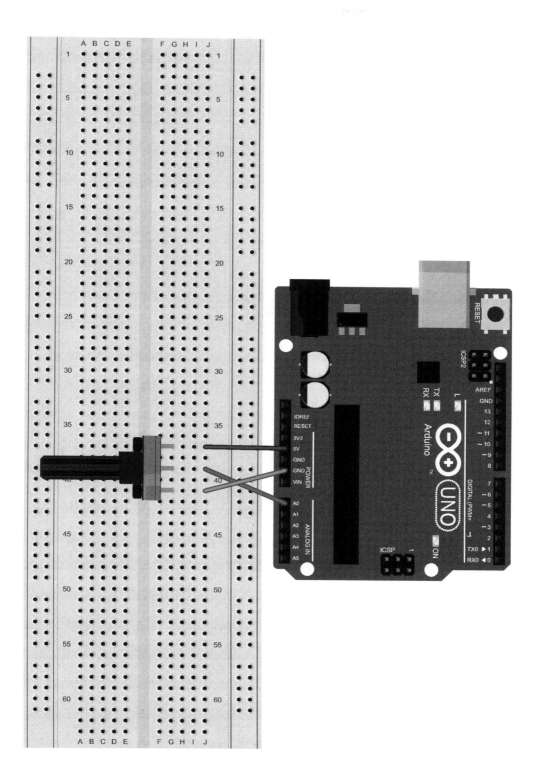

```
void setup() {
    // Initialize serial communication:
    Serial.begin(9600);
}


void loop() {
    // Read the sensor:
    int sensorReading = analogRead(A0);
    // Map the sensor range to a range of four options:
    int range = map(sensorReading, min, max, 0, 3);


    // Do something different depending on the range value:
    switch (range) {
        case 0:
            Serial.println("low");
            break;
        case 1:
            Serial.println("medium");
            break;
        case 2:
            Serial.println("high");
            break;
        case 3:
            Serial.println("ridiculous high");
            break;
    }

    delay(1);     // Delay in between reads for stability
}
```

DISCUSS THE SKETCH:

The first thing we want to take care of (as usual) is initializing and declaring variables for use throughout the program. We use two constant integers. These integers will be used to map the analog input range to a much smaller range to use with our *switch case* statement.

```
const int min = 0;      // Lowest reading at analog pin
const int max = 1023;   // Highest reading at analog pin
```

In setup(), all we need to do is begin serial communication using the begin() function from the Serial library. Easy enough.

Moving on to loop() we want to check our sensor value right off the bat, and assign it to a variable:

```
int sensorReading = analogRead(A0);
```

The analogRead() function reads the voltage at the specified analog pin. This value is assigned to an integer called *sensorReading*.

Every time through the loop, a new value will be assigned to this variable based on the value at analog pin A0. Recall that analogRead() returns a value in the range from 0 to 1023. That is 1024 distinct possibilities – we could make a *case* for each one if we were really crazed, but instead of that we will condense this range into a very small range of 0 through 3 using the map() function:

```
int range = map(sensorReading, sensorMin, sensorMax, 0, 3);
```

The map() function is used to convert a value from one range to another range. The map() function takes five arguments:

```
           1                    2                    3
map(Variable_to_be_Mapped, Low_Initial_Range, High_Initial_Range,
        4        5
    New_Low, New_High)
```

The output of the map() function converts the *Variable_to_be_Mapped* argument from it's initial range, to the new range.

The initial range we pass is 0 through 1023. The range we want to convert to is 0 through 3. This results in the following output values:

INPUT	→	OUTPUT
0–340	→	0
341–681	→	1
682–1022	→	2
1023	→	3

Take a long look at those input and output ranges - do you notice anything off?

You're probably thinking this doesn't make any sense! Here's the deal. The algorithm behind the map() function uses integer math. Integer math treats remainders a certain way. Any time there is any type of remainder, it's truncated. It doesn't get rounded. It just gets cut off.

As a result, the last number of the previousHigh always maps directly to the last value of the newHigh. So for a range that goes from zero to four, the only value that gets mapped to four is 1023 on the old range.

I know it seems really peculiar, but that's just how it works. Other than that rather curious behavior, the map() function works just like you would expect.

```
switch (range)
{
case 0:
   Serial.printIn("low");
   break;
case 1:
   Serial.printIn("medium");
   break;
case 2:
   Serial.printIn("high");
   break;
}
```

Variable you test against the cases.

The case either matches the variable or not.

If a case matches, the code for that case gets executed.

The break keyword lets the program know the case is complete.

Using this condensed range allows us to easily match 4 different cases – which is good because up next is our *switch case* statement:

```
switch (range) {
    case 0:
        Serial.println("low");
        break;
    case 1:
        Serial.println("medium");
        break;
    case 2:
        Serial.println("high");
        break;
    case 2:
        Serial.println("ridiculous high");
        break;
}
```

We see that we are testing our range variable against four different cases. Each case is followed by a simple println() function that will tell us where we have our potentiometer adjusted by sending text to the serial monitor window.

A quick note on sending text using the print() or println() functions – to let Arduino know you are sending text, you have to surround the text with quotation marks. Each letter has a number value assigned to it (called the ASCII coding) , if you forget the quotes, then it will send the numbers and not the text - more on this in the Further Reading suggestions.

Adjusting the potentiometer changes the voltage being applied at pin A0, this adjusts the reading captured by analogRead(). If the reading at A0 is 4, you will receive a "low", if it is 742, you will receive "high" and so forth for the different condensed ranges.

The break statement at the end of each case tells the Arduino to finish with the *switch case* and move on with the rest of the program.

The final touch to this program is putting a delay at the end of the loop() – this will allow the reading at the analog pin to stabilize before taking the next sample. Once the delay is complete we sample analog pin A0 again, map the range, and check for a matching case.

The *switch case* statement is a great programming tool when you want several specific values to trigger separate blocks of code.

TRY ON YOUR OWN CHALLENGE:

- Add an additional case to the *switch case* statement. You will have to expand the map() range to do this.

FURTHER READING:

Go to the Arduino Reference webpage and read the documentation on these functions.

https://www.arduino.cc/reference/en/

- switch…case
- char

Switch Case Statements and Keyboard Input

KEY POINTS:

1   This sketch demonstrates an alternate method of sequentially blinking a row of lights.

2   *default* can be added to a *switch case* statement as a catchall.

3   Serial.available() returns the number of bytes at the serial port.

How is it the QWERTY keyboard has been around so long? We used to "hunt & gather" now we "hunt & peck" (or at least I do).

It seems the keyboard is a long lasting human interface device that will be around for at least until the singularity, so we might as well make the best use of it.

This lesson introduces use of the keyboard to communicate with the Arduino. As in the last lesson, the primary function to accomplish this task is a *switch case* statement in cahoots with the read() function from the Serial library.

If you started this book at the beginning, then you are familiar will all the functions in this lesson. Here the functions are used in a slightly different application.

You type letters on the keyboard that are read by the Arduino and tested against different cases. If a letter matches a case, an LED lights for that case – if the letter does not match any cases, a *default* statement is used to turn off all the LEDs.

YOU WILL NEED:

1 220 ohm resistor (5)

2 LED (5)

3 Jumper wire (1)

4 Medium bag of chocolate candies (1)

STEP-BY-STEP INSTRUCTIONS:

1 Connect one side of a resistor to pin 2, connect the other side into a row on the breadboard.

2 Connect the long leg of the LED to the row in the breadboard where you attached the resistor.

3 Connect the short leg of the LED to one of the power strip columns on the breadboard.

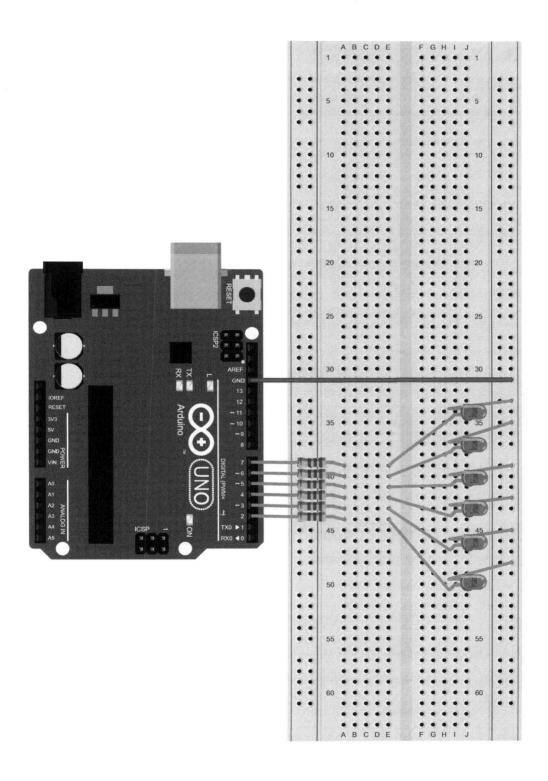

4   Now connect a resistor to pin 3, and put the other leg in a row on the breadboard (a different row then your first LED).

5   Connect an LED in the same manner – make sure the short leg goes in the SAME power strip column as the previous LED.

6   Repeat this through pin 6.

7   Using a jumper wire, connect the common power strip to a GND pin on the Arduino.

8   Connect the Arduino to your computer.

9   Open up the Arduino IED.

10   Open the sketch for this section.

11   Click the Verify button (check mark icon). The Arduino IDE will check your code for errors.

12   Open up the serial monitor from the menu bar Tools > Serial Monitor.

13   In the Send box of the serial monitor, type in a, b, c, d, or e and send it. Make sure "No Line Ending" is selected in the line ending drop down box.

THE ARDUINO CODE

```
/*
 * Switch statement with serial input
 * Demonstrates the use of a switch statement. The switch
 * statement allows you to choose from among a set of discrete
 * values of a variable. It's like a series of if statements.
```

```
 * To see this sketch in action, open the Serial monitor and
 * send any character. The characters a, b, c, d, and e, will
 * turn on LEDs. Any other character will turn the LEDs off.
 *
 * The circuit:
 * - 5 LEDs attached to digital pins 2 through 6 through
 *   220-ohm resistors
 *
 * This example code is in the public domain.
 */


void setup() {
    // Initialize serial communication:
    Serial.begin(9600);

    // Initialize the LED pins:
    for (int thisPin = 2; thisPin < 7; thisPin++) {
        pinMode(thisPin, OUTPUT);
    }
}


void loop() {
    // Read the sensor:
    if (Serial.available() > 0) {
        int inByte = Serial.read();
        // Do something different depending on the character
        // received. The switch statement expects single number
        // values for each case; in this example, though,
```

```
// you're using single quotes to tell the controller
// to get the ASCII value for the character.
// For example 'a' = 97, 'b' = 98, and so forth:

switch (inByte) {
case 'a':
    digitalWrite(2, HIGH);
    break;
case 'b':
    digitalWrite(3, HIGH);
    break;
case 'c':
    digitalWrite(4, HIGH);
    break;
case 'd':
    digitalWrite(5, HIGH);
    break;
case 'e':
    digitalWrite(6, HIGH);
    break;
default:
    // Turn all the LEDs off:
    for (int thisPin = 2; thisPin < 7; thisPin++) {
        digitalWrite(thisPin, LOW);
    }
    }
    }
}
```

DISCUSS THE SKETCH:

This sketch does not begin with any variable declarations – it jumps directly into the setup() function. It starts by opening serial communications with the begin() function from the Serial library. Then it moves to setting the mode of the pins using a *for loop* and the pinMode() function.

```
for (int thisPin = 2; thisPin < 7; thisPin++) {
    pinMode(thisPin, OUTPUT);
}
```

In this way, each pin with an LED attached is set as an OUTPUT. The *for loop* method of initializing pins should be familiar - check out the For Loop Iteration section to brush up if you need to.

Once complete with setup() we move to the body of the code in the loop() function. Start the *for loop* with an *if statement* – a pretty important one at that – everything inside the loop depends on the *if statement*. If the condition in the *if statement* is not met – nothing new happens at all! So what is the condition of this power mongering *if statement*?

```
if (Serial.available() > 0)
```

This condition implements a function called available() from the Serial library. The available() function checks at the serial port to see if any bytes are available and returns the number of bytes. If bytes are available the condition of the *if statement* will be met because Serial.available() will return a number larger than 0.

So why would bytes be available?

In this case, we are sending bytes to the serial port using the Arduino IDE serial monitor send functionality. Each character we send has an associated numerical value – called its ASCII value – which is one byte. When you send the lowercase letter 'c' for example, the number 99 will be sent to the serial port.

This condition asks, "Has a value been sent to the serial port?" If the answer is yes, then the *if statement* is executed, if the answer in no, then the *if statement* is ignored. So what happens if a value was sent?

The first thing we want to do, is read the data at the serial port. We do this with the read() function from the Serial library:

```
int inByte = Serial.read();
```

We create an integer variable called *inByte* and we let it equal the value read at the serial port. If we had typed 'c', then the value of *inByte* would be 99. If we had typed 'x', the value of *inByte* would be assigned 120. Once this value is captured in a variable, we need to test to see if it is one of the letters we want. If it is a letter we are looking for, then we light up an LED, if not then we turn off all the LEDs.

A *switch case* statement is just the tool for this job:

```
switch (inByte) {
case 'a':
    digitalWrite(2, HIGH);
    break;
case 'b':
    digitalWrite(3, HIGH);
    break;
case 'c':
    digitalWrite(4, HIGH);
    break;
case 'd':
    digitalWrite(5, HIGH);
    break;
case 'e':
    digitalWrite(6, HIGH);
    break;
default:
    // Turn all the LEDs off:
    for (int thisPin = 2; thisPin < 7; thisPin++) {
        digitalWrite(thisPin, LOW);
    }
}
```

The *switch case* statement compares the value of *inByte* to five different cases. If the case is met, then its code turns on the LED at a specified pin using digitalWrite(). If a match is not found, we use an awesome feature of the *switch case* statement called a *default*.

default allows us to have a back up plan if the incoming byte does not match any of the cases. In this default statement we use a *for loop* to digitally write LOW voltage to all the pins:

```
for (int thisPin = 2; thisPin < 7; thisPin++) {
    digitalWrite(thisPin, LOW);
}
```

This *switch case* allows us to turn on different LEDs using specific "commands", and turns off all the LEDs when an input does not match one of the specified commands.

Please notice the closing curly braces at the end of this program. There are a ton! How can you tell which one is which? It can get confusing - often what I do is use comments at the end of curly braces to identify its corresponding function:

```
        } // Close for loop
      } // Close switch case
    } // Close if statement
} // Close loop()
```

For some people this is a little much, but I find it helps me keep all the closing curly braces straight. When we have functions that operate inside other functions, like the *switch case* statement inside the *if statement*, this is called *nesting*.

Nesting allows us to add layers of logic to our programs, but can get a little confusing if you start going overboard with your nested statements.

TRY ON YOUR OWN CHALLENGE:

● Add an additional case to the *switch case* statement that will turn on all the LEDs with one keystroke.

● Add a sixth LED at pin 7 and a case that will illuminate it.

FURTHER READING:

Go to the Arduino Reference webpage and read the documentation on these functions.

https://www.arduino.cc/reference/en/

● Serial.available()

● Serial.read()

CHAPTER

04

DIGITAL

You are ready to tackle some more complicated designs - to do this you need a couple more techniques to implement your ideas. This chapter provides some of the nitty-gritty details required to make seemingly simple circuits work like you want them too. Be prepared to use some brain power, as this chapter is all about the details.

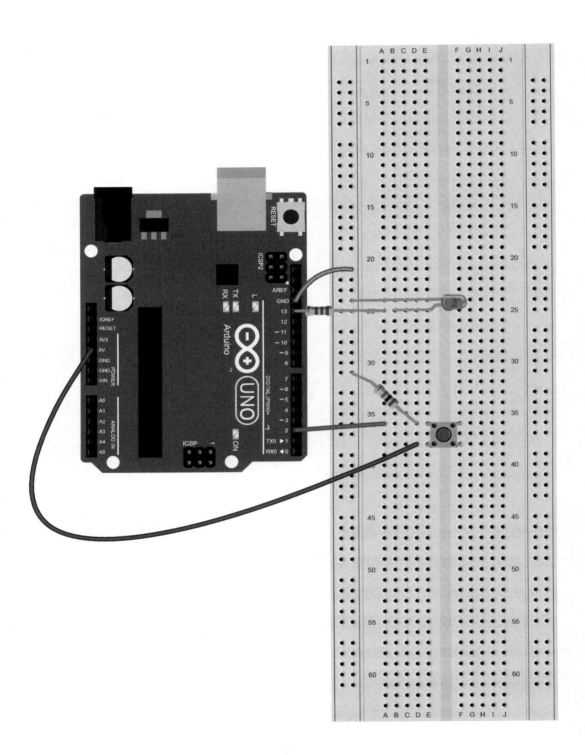

Blink an LED Without Using the delay() Function

KEY POINTS:

1   Using the delay() function can adversely affect the operation of your program.

2   The millis() function returns the number of milliseconds since the sketch started running on your Arduino.

3   millis() can be used in place of delay() for timing of certain events.

4   *long* is a data type that stores very large whole numbers - it takes a lot of space compared to an integer and should be used only when necessary.

I am reminded of the famous idiom "There is more than one way to blink an LED." Which holds very true for the Arduino platform. You should know at least four ways to blink an LED with your Arduino by the end of this course.

So what is the big deal about using the delay() function? In the first lesson we used delay() between digitalWrite() to keep an LED lit for about one second and off for about one second. If it works, why fix it? Well, it does work, but there are alternatives to using it and reasons why.

A good reason NOT to use delay() is that it stops the entire program in its tracks. If you are trying to read information at the serial port or gather data at an analog pin – all these important tasks are stopped.

It's like the game Green Light / Red Light, when your friend pretends to be a stoplight and every time she yells "Red Light" every one has to stop in their tracks. The delay() function loves this game – but all the other functions get sick of it after about two rounds of play.

In this lesson we explore using the Arduino's built in clock to determine timing for events to start and stop.

YOU WILL NEED:

1 LED (1)

2 220 ohm resistor (1)

3 Alligator clip (1)

4 Brass scissors, slightly dull (1)

NOTE: Technically you do not need any external hardware, because we will use pin 13, and on most Arduino boards there is an LED attached to the board. I like the external stuff, but it's up to you.

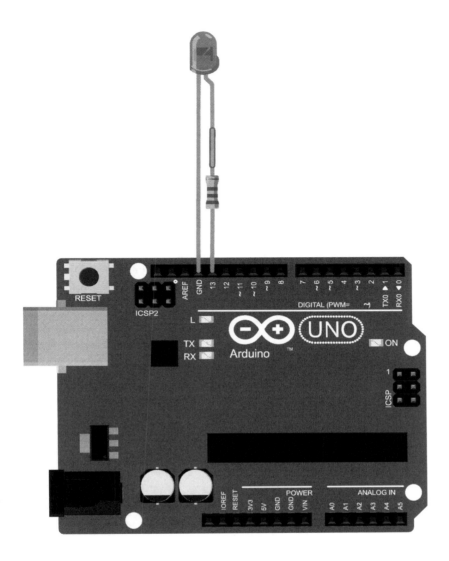

STEP-BY-STEP INSTRUCTIONS:

1. Insert the long leg of the LED into pin 13 on your Arduino.

2. Connect the 220 ohm resistor to the ground pin on the Arduino (the one next to pin 13 labeled GND is the most convenient). It doesn't matter which way you connect the resistor.

(3) Now use the alligator clip to connect the short leg of the LED to the other leg of the resistor. If you do not have an alligator clip, you can twist the two leads together as best you can to get a steady electrical connection.

(4) Plug the Arduino board into your computer with a USB cable.

(5) Open up the Arduino IDE.

(6) Open the sketch for this section.

(7) Click the Verify button on the top left. It should turn orange and then back to blue.

(8) Click the Upload button. It will also turn orange and then blue once the sketch has finished uploading to your Arduino board.

(9) Now monitor the Arduino board - the LED at pin 13 should be blinking.

THE ARDUINO CODE:

```
/*
 * Blink without Delay
 * Turns on and off a light emitting diode(LED) connected to
 * a digital pin, without using the delay() function. This means
 * that other code can run at the same time without being
 * interrupted by the LED code.
 *
 * The circuit:
 * - LED attached from pin 13 to ground.
 *
```

```
 * Note: on most Arduinos, there is already an LED on the board
 * that's attached to pin 13, so no hardware is needed for
 * this example.
 *
 * This example code is in the public domain.
 */



// Constants won't change. Used here to set pin numbers:
const int ledPin = 13;     // The number of the LED pin

// Variables will change:
int ledState = LOW;        // ledState used to set the LED
long previousMillis = 0;   // Will store last time LED was updated

// The follow variables is a long because the time, measured in
// milliseconds, will quickly become a bigger number than can be
// stored in an int.
long interval = 1000; // Interval at which to blink (milliseconds)


void setup() {
    // Set the digital pin as output:
    pinMode(ledPin, OUTPUT);
}


void loop() {
    // Here is where you'd put code that needs to be running
    // all the time.
```

```
// Check to see if it's time to blink the LED; that is,
// if the difference between the current time and last time
// you blinked the LED is bigger than the interval at which
// you want to blink the LED.
unsigned long currentMillis = millis();

if (currentMillis - previousMillis > interval) {
    // Save the last time you blinked the LED
    previousMillis = currentMillis;

    // If the LED is off turn it on and vice-versa:
    if (ledState == LOW) {
        ledState = HIGH;
    } else {
        ledState = LOW;
    }

    // Set the LED with the ledState of the variable:
    digitalWrite(ledPin, ledState);
  }
}
```

DISCUSS THE SKETCH:

As sketches get longer and more involved they can be difficult to follow. I try to look at things in small of chunks. Taking the time to read the comments helps considerably.

This program starts by declaring and initializing a couple useful variables. The first one is *ledPin*, which will be used to hold the

LED pin number, and is qualified as a *constant*. Recall that *const* is a qualifier which protects a variable from ever being changed by the program:

```
const int ledPin = 13;      // The number of the LED pin
```

We also use an integer variable to store the state of the LED:

```
int ledState = LOW;         // ledState used to set the LED
```

The next variables are declared as *longs*. A *long* is a data type just like an integer, except that it can hold a much larger number. The idea is to use the smallest data type for a given job, that way memory space isn't wasted. The integer value type can store a number in the range from (-)32,768 to (+) 32,767 which is good for many applications.

In this program, however, we will be storing milliseconds of time as it accumulates when the program first starts. The number will be gigantic, so we will need a bigger data type to hold this value, hence we use a *long* which stores a number from (-)2,147,483,648 to as high as (+)2,147,483,647 – nice and hefty!

```
long previousMillis = 0;   // Will store last time LED was updated
long interval = 1000; // Interval at which to blink (milliseconds)
```

Once the variables are declared we move to the setup() which simply sets the mode of pin 13 as an OUTPUT using the pinMode() function. After this we move on to loop().

The loop() functions opens with a variable declaration and initialization using the millis() function:

```
unsigned long currentMillis = millis();
```

What's going on here? First, let's look at the variable type we are making – it is an *unsigned long*. *Unsigned* is a qualifier of the variable *currentMillis*. If a variable is *signed* that means it can hold negative and positive values. Just as we said previously that a *long* can hold a range from negative 2,147,483,648 to positive 2,147,483,647 – the unsigned qualifier says " heck with the negative, I just want positive values". This allows for double the number of positive values to be stored in a *long* – thus an *unsigned long* can hold a number from 0 to 4,294,967,295 – that's four billion and some change, not too shabby.

What does this giant variable need to store? It will store the output of the function millis(). millis() returns the number of milliseconds from when the program started running based on the internal clock of the microcontroller. If you plugged your Arduino in and pressed the reset button, exactly one second later millis() would return the value 1000. If you waited 5.5 seconds, millis() would return 5500. Again, millis() returns the current clock value, which begins to count up at the start of the program. Any time you press the RESET button on the Arduino, the millis() function will start back at zero and start counting up again.

At the beginning of every loop this code captures the amount of time the sketch has been running and saves it in the variable *currentMillis*:

```
unsigned long currentMillis = millis();
```

What can we do with the current time? We use it to see if a certain amount of time has elapsed – if it *has* elapsed we turn on or off an LED, if it *has not* elapsed we ignore the code. The *if statement* is the perfect tool for this job:

```
if (currentMillis - previousMillis > interval) {
    // Save the last time you blinked the LED
    previousMillis = currentMillis;

    // If the LED is off turn it on and vice-versa:
    if (ledState == LOW){
        ledState = HIGH;
    } else {
        ledState = LOW;
    }
    // Set the LED with the ledState of the variable:
    digitalWrite(ledPin, ledState);
}
```

Let's take a close look at the *if statement* condition:

```
if (currentMillis - previousMillis > interval)
```

At the beginning of the program we set the variable *previousMillis* to 0, and the variable *interval* to 1000.

We know that the variable *currentMillis* is the current time, and we know that the variable *previousMillis* starts at 0. We take the current time and subtract the previous time, and check to see if this is greater than the interval time. This is how we check to see how much time has elapsed since the last time we lit or darkened our LED.

Keep in mind that the Arduino goes through this loop() super fast, as in many, many times per millisecond. Let's say the first time through the loop() the millis() function returns a one. Since one minus zero is less then 1000, nothing happens. It will not be until after at least 1000 milliseconds that the condition of the *if statement* is met and the code in the *if statement* is executed.

Once the if statement starts it assigns the *currentMillis* value to the *previousMillis* value:

```
previousMillis = currentMillis;
```

This updates the *previousMillis* variable, so that it can track when the *if statement* was last executed. Think of *previousMillis* as the variable that says "The last time the *if statement* was executed was XYZ time". In this way, *previousMillis* keeps an updated account of when the state of the LED last changed.

After we update the times, we encounter another *if statement*. This next *if statement* checks whether the LED is on or off, using the *ledState* variable as its test condition:

```
if (ledState == LOW){
    ledState = HIGH;
} else {
    ledState = LOW;
}
```

If *ledState* is LOW, this code simply changes it to HIGH, otherwise it sets the state as LOW. In this way, each time this *if statement* is executed, it toggles the state of the LED – which creates a blinking effect.

But to actually blink the LED we need to change the voltage at pin 13, this is done immediately after the close of the *if statement* using digitalWrite():

```
digitalWrite(ledPin, ledState);
```

As you know, digitalWrite() requires two arguments 1) the pin number and 2) the state. We use variables to assign both of these arguments. *ledPin* was assigned as 13 at the beginning of the program and *ledState* is what was just flip flopped by the previous *if statement*.

Let's review each step this sketch performs:

1 Check to see if a certain interval of time has elapsed.

2 If the interval *has* elapsed we assign the current time to the previous time.

3 Flip the state of the variable *ledState*.

4 Turn the LED on or off based on *ledState* using digitalWrite().

That seems like an awful lot of work to blink an LED – but now you are free to sample other parameters on your board instead of waiting for the delay() function to give you the same effect.

TRY ON YOUR OWN CHALLENGE:

• Adjust the *interval* variable

• Add a potentiometer to this circuit and add some code to this sketch to read and display the input value. Now do the same thing with a different sketch just using the delay function to blink the LED - can you see the difference?

FURTHER READING:

Go to the Arduino Reference webpage and read the documentation on these functions.

https://www.arduino.cc/reference/en/

• millis()

• unsigned long

• unsigned int

Using a Button with Arduino

KEY POINTS:

1 A *momentary button* is not like an On/Off switch - it is only engaged when you press it, otherwise it springs back to its neutral state.

Anything cool has buttons. They are everywhere and there is certain pleasure in pressing them. Knowing how to employ them in your projects is very beneficial. Using a button is as easy as you might think, but at the same time can be a source of frustration.

In this example we simply hook up 5 volts to one side of a button and to the other side of the button we connect pin 2. When you press the button it completes an electrical connection, pin 2 will "see" the 5 volts and if we digitalRead() at pin 2, it will report HIGH. During the times the button is not being pressed, pin 2 reports LOW.

To turn on an LED by pressing the button, we simply make an *if statement* whose condition says something like "...if the voltage at pin 2 is HIGH, turn on the LED at pin 13..." It is really that easy.

We also have pin 2 connected to ground at all times through a resistor. This is because when we read values at pin 2, we want to get either a HIGH or a LOW reported. If pin 2 is not connected to ground, then when the button is not being pressed it becomes what is called a *floating pin* – it's not connected to anything. Floating pins on the Arduino are fine for the most part – unless you are trying to record an input from them – then they are bad, and can give you spurious information. Check the supplemental video lessons for a video which demonstrates why the resistor keeping pin 2 at ground is essential.

YOU WILL NEED:

1. LED (1)
2. 10k ohm resistor (1)
3. 220 ohm resistor (1)
4. Pushbutton (1)
5. Jumper wires (3)
6. Green apple (1)

STEP-BY-STEP INSTRUCTIONS:

1 Connect one of the Arduino GND pins to one of the long power rails on the breadboard – this will be the ground rail.

2 Connect the short leg of the LED to this same ground rail on the breadboard then connect the long leg to a row on the breadboard.

3 Connect the 220 ohm resistor from pin 13 to the same row that you have the long leg of the LED attached.

4 Place the pushbutton on the breadboard. Most buttons will straddle the center trench on the breadboard.

5 Connect a jumper wire from the 5-volt pin to one side of the pushbutton.

6 Connect a jumper wire from pin 2 to the other side of the pushbutton.

7 Connect one side of the 10k resistor from the ground rail on the breadboard to the other side to the pushbutton – on the same side that pin 2 connects.

8 Plug the Arduino board into your computer with a USB cable.

9 Open the Arduino IDE.

10 Open the sketch for this section.

11 Click the Verify button (check mark icon). The Arduino IDE will check your code for errors.

12 Click the Upload button (right arrow icon). You will see the TX and RX LEDs on your Arduino board begin to flash rapidly.

13 Press the button a couple times and see how the LED at pin 13 reacts.

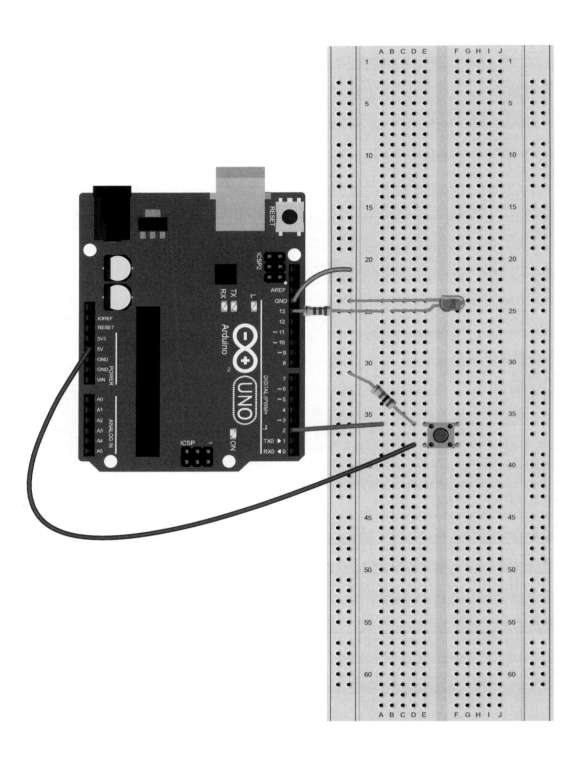

THE ARDUINO CODE:

```
/*
 * Button
 * Turns on and off a light emitting diode(LED) connected to
 * digital pin 13, when pressing a pushbutton attached to pin 2.
 *
 * The circuit:
 * - LED attached from pin 13 to ground
 * - pushbutton attached to pin 2 from +5V
 * - 10K resistor attached to pin 2 from ground
 *
 * Note: on most Arduinos there is already an LED on the board
 * attached to pin 13.
 *
 * This example code is in the public domain.
 */



// Constants won't change. They're used here to set pin numbers:
const int buttonPin = 2;    // The number of the pushbutton pin
const int ledPin = 13;      // The number of the LED pin


// Variables will change:
int buttonState = 0;
    // Variable for reading the pushbutton status


void setup() {
    // Initialize the LED pin as an output:
    pinMode(ledPin, OUTPUT);
```

```
  // Initialize the pushbutton pin as an input:
  pinMode(buttonPin, INPUT);
}


void loop() {
  // Read the state of the pushbutton value:
  buttonState = digitalRead(buttonPin);

  // Check if the pushbutton is pressed.
  // If it is, the buttonState is HIGH:
  if (buttonState == HIGH) {
    // Turn LED on:
    digitalWrite(ledPin, HIGH);
  } else {
    // Turn LED off:
    digitalWrite(ledPin, LOW);
  }
}
```

DISCUSS THE SKETCH:

A word to the wise, read the whole sketch before going further. Reading code can make your brain hurt, but it gets less painful over time.

This sketch starts with declaring and initializing variable constants that define which pins are used for the button and LED.

```
const int buttonPin = 2;    // The number of the pushbutton pin
const int ledPin = 13;      // The number of the LED pin
```

The only other variable required to make this sketch work is a variable to track the status of pin 2 – we want to know if pin 2 is HIGH or LOW.

```
int buttonState = 0; // Variable for reading the pushbutton status
```

With the variables accounted for we now move on to the setup() of the sketch. We need to let the Arduino know we will be using pin 2 as an INPUT and pin 13 as an OUTPUT.

```
void setup() {
    // Initialize the LED pin as an output:
    pinMode(ledPin, OUTPUT);
    // Initialize the pushbutton pin as an input:
    pinMode(buttonPin, INPUT);
}
```

That's a pretty easy setup(). As a reminder, the pins on an Arduino are set by default as INPUTs, so we do not need to explicitly use the pinMode() function as done here. I explicitly set them as INPUTs however, in order to make clear my intention to use the pin as an INPUT. Some may think this a bit overboard, but it suits me well.

The first line of code in the loop() reads the state of pin 2 and assigns the value to our *buttonState* variable:

```
buttonState = digitalRead(buttonPin);
// Read the state of the pushbutton value:
```

As you may recall, the digitalRead() function returns the value, either HIGH or LOW, of the pin you put in the parenthesis. In this example, if the button is pressed, then 5 volts is applied to the pin and the digitalRead() function will return HIGH – and this value is stored in the *buttonState* variable. When the button is not pressed, digitalRead() will return LOW because it is connected to ground.

Now that we know what the button is up to, we can use an *if statement* condition to add functionality:

```
if (buttonState == HIGH) {
    // Turn LED on:
    digitalWrite(ledPin, HIGH);
} else {
    // Turn LED off:
    digitalWrite(ledPin, LOW);
}
```

This *if-else statement* says, "If the button is being pressed turn the LED on otherwise turn it off." The code executed by the *if-else statement* turns the LED on or off by using the digitalWrite() function.

The steps this loop() accomplishes are:

1 Checks the state of the button.

2 Turns the LED on or off according to the HIGH or LOW state.

This sketch is simple yet powerful. It demonstrates what you can do with some basic programming and microcontroller know-how.

TRY ON YOUR OWN CHALLENGE:

• Can you make the LED at pin 13 blink rapidly when you hold the button down?

• Attach another LED to pin 12. Change the code so that both LEDs illuminate with the button press.

FURTHER READING:

Go to the Arduino Reference webpage and read the documentation on these functions.

https://www.arduino.cc/reference/en/

• digitalRead()

SUPPLEMENTAL VIDEO LESSONS

View these on the Programming Electronics Academy training portal.

Floating Pins

State Change Detection and the Modulo Operator

KEY POINTS:

1   You may not always have a piece of hardware available to implement a solution - you might be able to use software to bridge the gap.

2   For our purposes, a *state change* is the moment in time when a pin goes from LOW voltage to HIGH voltage, or vice versa.

3   The *Modulo Operator* (%) returns the remainder of a division. It can be used to make a repeating count.

In the last example, you learned how to employ a button with the Arduino. When you pressed and held it down things happened, and when you released it different things happened.

But there lies a blaring problem if you just want an on/off switch – namely, who is going to keep the button pressed when you get tired?

There are lots of buttons available. Some buttons will hold themselves down – press it, and it sticks and maintains contact between two wires. This type of button is a hardware solution to the "Who will hold the button?" dilemma.

We used a pushbutton in the last example – a type of momentary switch that connects two wires *when you hold it down*. What this lesson seeks to explore is how we can use a momentary pushbutton to work as an on/off switch by using clever code.

Let's think about what happens when you press a button. In this example (and the last) we have a digital pin connected to 5 volts through a pushbutton. When we push the button, the 5 volts are applied to the digital pin. At one moment there is 0 voltage at the pin, and at the next moment there are 5 volts at the pin. When you release the button the pin goes back to 0 voltage. Consider the figure on the next page:

What we will do is write a program that says "when the voltage changes from 0 to 5 volts, then do something, otherwise don't do jack". This change in voltage creates what is referred to as an "edge" and this sketch performs what is called *edge detection*.

An on/off button is useful, but to keep things interesting this program will require four button presses to turn on an LED. Adding this layer of complexity allows us to explore another interesting programming tool called the *modulo operator*.

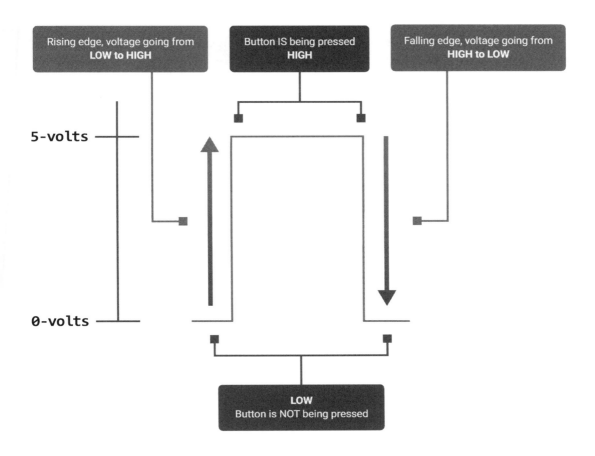

YOU WILL NEED:

1. LED (1)

2. 10k ohm resistor (1)

3. 220 ohm resistor (1)

4. Momentary pushbutton (1)

5. Jumper wires (3)

6. Short sleeve flannel shirt (with buttons)

STEP-BY-STEP INSTRUCTIONS:

1 Connect one of the Arduino GND pins to one of the long power rails on the breadboard – this will be the ground rail.

2 Connect the short leg of the LED to this same ground rail on the breadboard. Connect the long leg to any inside row on the breadboard.

3 Connect a 220 ohm resistor from pin 13 to the same row where the long leg of the LED is attached.

4 Place the pushbutton on the breadboard.

5 Connect a jumper wire from the 5 volt pin to one side of the pushbutton.

6 Connect a jumper wire from pin 2 to the other side of the pushbutton.

7 Connect one side of a 10k resistor to the ground rail on the breadboard. Connect the other side of the 10k resistor to the pushbutton – on the same side that pin 2 connects.

8 Plug the Arduino board into your computer with a USB cable.

9 Open up the Arduino IDE.

10 Open the sketch for this section.

11 Click the Verify button (check mark icon). The Arduino IDE will check your code for errors.

12 Click the Upload button (right arrow icon). You will see the TX and RX LEDs on your Arduino board begin to flash rapidly.

13 Open up the serial monitor window.

14 Press the button a couple times and see how the LED at pin 13 reacts.

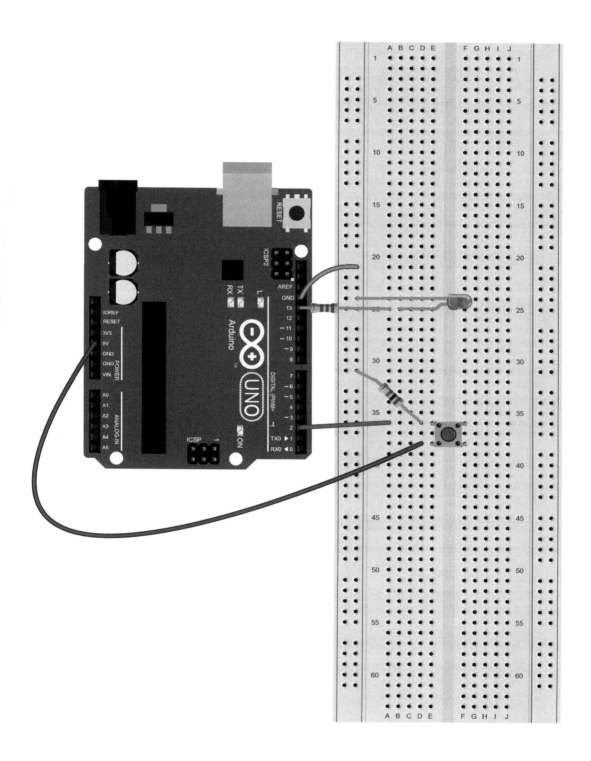

THE ARDUINO CODE:

```
/*
 * State change detection (edge detection)
 * Often, you don't need to know the state of a digital input
 * all the time, but you just need to know when the input changes
 * from one state to another. For example, you want to know when
 * a button goes from OFF to ON. This is called state change
 * detection, or edge detection.
 * This example shows how to detect when a button or button
 * changes from off to on and on to off.
 *
 * The circuit:
 * - pushbutton attached to pin 2 from +5V
 * - 10K resistor attached to pin 2 from ground
 * - LED attached from pin 13 to ground (or use the built-in LED
 *   on most Arduino boards)
 *
 * This example code is in the public domain.
 */


// This constant won't change:
const int buttonPin = 2;
    // The pin that the pushbutton is attached to
const int ledPin = 13;
    // The pin that the LED is attached to


// Variables will change:
int buttonPushCounter = 0;
    // Counter for the number of button presses
```

```
int buttonState = 0;
   // Current state of the button
int lastButtonState = 0;
   // Previous state of the button


void setup() {
   // Initialize the button pin as a input:
   pinMode(buttonPin, INPUT);
   // Initialize the LED as an output:
   pinMode(ledPin, OUTPUT);
   // Initialize serial communication:
   Serial.begin(9600);
}


void loop() {
   // Read the pushbutton input pin:
   buttonState = digitalRead(buttonPin);

   // Compare the buttonState to its previous state
   if (buttonState != lastButtonState) {
      // If the state has changed, increment the counter
      if (buttonState == HIGH) {
         // If the current state is HIGH then the button
         // went from off to on:
         buttonPushCounter++;
         Serial.println("on");
         Serial.print("number of button pushes: ");
         Serial.println(buttonPushCounter);
      }
```

```
    else {
        // If the current state is LOW then the button
        // went from on to off:
        Serial.println("off");
    }
}


// Save the current state as the last state,
// For next time through the loop
lastButtonState = buttonState;

// Turns on the LED every four button pushes by checking the
// modulo of the button push counter. The modulo function
// gives you the remainder of the division of two numbers:
if (buttonPushCounter % 4 == 0) {
    digitalWrite(ledPin, HIGH);
} else {
    digitalWrite(ledPin, LOW);
}
}
```

DISCUSS THE SKETCH:

This is the most complicated sketch thus far. Remember, the best way to keep long programs straight in your mind is to break them up into manageable chunks. The big chunks (called code blocks) in just about any Arduino sketch are the variable declaration and initializations, the setup(), and the loop(). Function definitions will be added to this list as the sketches become more complex.

In addition, you can start subdividing code in the loop() into sepa-rate chunks – consider the chunks as separate functional units. You could think, "Ok, this *if statement* accomplishes XYZ task, or this *for loop* performs ABC task." If you don't mentally Kung-Fu chop the code into pieces, then trying to juggle all the different moving parts in your head becomes unwieldy.

Let's first consider the variables declared and initialized. The vari-ables used as pins are qualified as *constants* and all the others are *integers* used to track the state of the button:

```
const int buttonPin = 2;
    // The pin that the pushbutton is attached to
const int ledPin = 13;
    // The pin that the LED is attached to
int buttonPushCounter = 0;
    // Counter for the number of button presses
int buttonState = 0;
    // Current state of the button
int lastButtonState = 0;
    // Previous state of the button
```

The names of these variables infer their purpose, but as we dive into the code, each will make more sense.

The setup() for this sketch is standard fair – we need to set the pin modes and initiate serial communication with the serial port. We use the pinMode() and Serial.begin() functions to accom-plish this:

```
void setup() {
    // Initialize the button pin as a input:
    pinMode(buttonPin, INPUT);
    // Initialize the LED as an output:
    pinMode(ledPin, OUTPUT);
    // Initialize serial communication:
    Serial.begin(9600);
}
```

On a quick aside, notice that we almost always use variables to define pin numbers – or any number for that matter in a sketch – even if we only use the variable once. Why not just type the value of the pin in the pinMode() function?

The reason is that variables provide flexibility. It's tempting to type the hardcoded number if you think it will only be used once in the sketch. But what if you realize that using that hardcoded number later down the sketch is advisable – now you have 2 hardcoded numbers – and before you know it by the end of the program instead of typing that hardcoded number once you have typed it five times. Then, if you want to change the value you will have to track down all the hard coded numbers – and I bet you will miss one – I always do.

As a rule of thumb, unless you absolutely, positively know that you will not change the value and that it will only be typed once – then use a variable. The baud rate 9600 that is used for Serial.begin() is a pretty stable number, an example of where hardcoding makes sense. There are few examples like this – because variables are better than numbers.

Moving on to the loop(). We start by sampling the state of the digital pin where the pushbutton is attached. We want to know from the very start – is the button being pressed at this instant? The digitalRead() function returns a HIGH or LOW which is then stored in the *buttonState* variable:

```
buttonState = digitalRead(buttonPin);
// Read the pushbutton input pin:
```

After we have sampled the *buttonPin* the first thing to ask is, "Has the state of the pin changed since we checked it last?" This is determined with an *if statement*:

```
if (buttonState != lastButtonState) {
```

In the first step we stored the current *buttonState*, now we compare it with the *lastButtonState* using the *NOT* operator which is written as != in Arduino code. The != means "not equal to". This condition says, "If the current button state does not equal the previous button state, then do something."

If the button state is the same the condition is not met, and the code enclosed by the *if statement* is skipped. This *if statement* condition only executes when the state has changed. The first time through the loop() the *lastButtonState* variable equals zero (recall we initiated it at the top as zero), which is equivalent to LOW.

If this sketch was running on the Arduino for a couple seconds - and you *press* the button - this *if statement* would be executed. This is because the *buttonState* was LOW and when you press the button it changed to HIGH.

Now when you *release* the button, the state of the pin changes from HIGH to LOW – therefore the *release* of the button engages the *if statement* as well. These voltage transitions from HIGH to LOW are called state changes. This code is one example of a *state change detector*.

What code is executed inside the curly brackets of the *if statement* when a *state change* is detected?

The first thing encountered is a nested *if-else statement*:

```
if (buttonState != lastButtonState) {
    if (buttonState == HIGH) {
        // If the current state is HIGH then the button
        // went from off to on:
        buttonPushCounter++;   // This just adds one to the value
        Serial.println("on");
        Serial.print("number of button pushes: ");
        Serial.println(buttonPushCounter);
    } else {
        // If the current state is LOW then the button
        // went from on to off:
        Serial.println("off");
    }
}
```

The condition of the nested *if statement* is:

```
if (buttonState == HIGH)
```

To visualize this condition consider the actual button in its resting state (LOW), now imagine it has been pressed (HIGH). *This if statement* condition checks if *buttonState* changed from LOW to HIGH.

When the *if statement* condition is met:

1. *buttonPushCounter* is incremented (the ++ just adds 1 to the variable)

2. Information is sent to the serial port for display on the serial monitor window

The information sent to the serial monitor lets us know what the program is up to – it tells us how many times we pressed the button and the current *buttonState* value.

When the button is *released* – the pin state changes from HIGH to LOW and now the value read and assigned to the *buttonState* variable will be LOW. Because a value of LOW does not satisfy the *if statement* condition, the next code block executed is inside the *else statement*. All this code does is print some info to the serial monitor that lets you know the current button state is LOW.

Thus far the process in the loop() can be summarized as follows:

1. Was the button pressed or released?

2 If the button was pressed, the code will:

i Increment the *buttonPushCounter* variable by 1

ii Print out information about the state of the button and the number of times it was pushed

3 If the button was released:

iv Print the state of the button

That's all there is to these seemingly complex nested *if statements*.

The next line of code we encounter is immediately after the close of the nested *if statements*. This code updates the *lastButtonState* variable:

```
lastButtonState = buttonState;
    // Assign the current button state to the last button state
```

When the loop() starts again it compares the *lastButtonState* variable with the current sampled *buttonState* variable. In this way, we are always comparing the preceding state of the button to the current state of the button.

The final block of code in this sketch is what turns the LED on and off. Recall that it will take four button presses to turn the LED on. That is why we are tracking button presses. If the button has been pressed four times – turn the LED on, otherwise, turn it off. One way to implement this process is with an *if-else statement*:

```
if (buttonPushCounter % 4 == 0) {
    digitalWrite(ledPin, HIGH);
} else {
    digitalWrite(ledPin, LOW);
}
```

The condition used in this *if statement* is new and a little funky. The percent sign symbol is called the *modulo operator*.

```
if (buttonPushCounter % 4 == 0)
```

To understand what this condition means we need to learn how the modulo operator works.

The modulo operator returns the remainder of an integer division.

Uhhhh…say what? Here is the deal, remember back in elementary school math class when you used remainders because decimals and fractions were too advanced for you?

Integer division (that is dividing two *int* variables with each other) works in the same manner, we do not use decimal points or fractions, but we are left with remainders.

If you divided 2 into 5, what would be the remainder?

⟶ 5/2 = 2 remainder 1

Two goes into 5 twice with 1 left over.

What if you divide 17 by 5?

⟶ 17/5 = 3 remainder 2

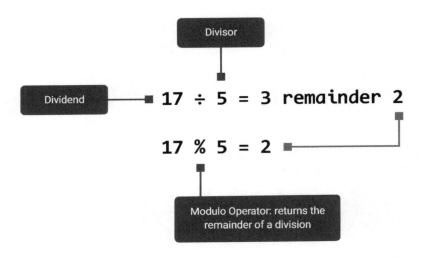

Ok, what if you divide 1 by 4? Remember, we are dealing only with integers here – not decimals or fractions.

⟶ 1 / 4 = 0 remainder 1.

Four does not go into one at all – it's too big – the remainder is 1 (one is what remains of the dividend).

⟶ 2 / 4 = 0 remainder 2

⟶ 3 / 4 = 0 remainder 3

⟶ 4 / 4 = 1 remainder 0

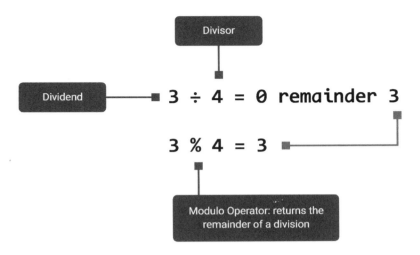

Take a look at the following calculations and see if you can follow along:

$\longrightarrow$ 5 % 2 = 1

$\longrightarrow$ 17 % 5 = 2

$\longrightarrow$ 1 % 4 = 1

$\longrightarrow$ 2 % 4 = 2

$\longrightarrow$ 3 % 4 = 3

$\longrightarrow$ 4 % 4 = 0

I like to think of the dividend as a container of ice cream, and the divisor as an ice cream scoop. How many even scoops can I get out of the ice cream container with a given size scoop? What ever is left in the ice cream container is the remainder – and this is what the modulo operator returns – it's like the spoon that reaches down to get the stubborn ice cream in the corner of the container. If my ice cream scoop is too big to get any ice cream out of the container, then the whole container is the remainder.

Let's look at the *if statement* condition again:

```
if (buttonPushCounter % 4 == 0)
```

Recall that the variable *buttonPushCounter* is keeping tally of how many times we have pressed the button – this condition asks "If I divide the number of times the button has been pressed by 4, is the remainder equal to zero?" The only time this condition will be met is when 4 divides evenly into *pushButtonCounter* – and there is no remainder. So the ice cream scoop perfectly gets all the ice cream – none is left over. The values 4, 8, 12, 24 or any multiple of 4 will satisfy this requirement.

What the modulo operator allows us to do is maintain a cycle. Look at the calculations below and see if you can follow along:

CALCULATION	THE MODULO OPERATOR RETURNS THE REMINDER OF AN INTEGER DIVISION.
1 % 4 = 1	One divided by four equals 0 remainder 1
2 % 4 = 2	Two divided by four equals 0 remainder 2
3 % 4 = 3	Three divided by four equals 0 remainder 3
4 % 4 = 0	Four divided by four equals 1 remainder 0
5 % 4 = 1	
6 % 4 = 2	
7 % 4 = 3	You can see that modulo operator cycles through – the remainder always stays less than the divisor by 1.
8 % 4 = 0	
9 % 4 = 1	
10 % 4 = 2	

As the chart demonstrates, the modulo operator starts back at zero every fourth calculation. We can use this cycle to turn on the LED every fourth button press.

Let's consider the final *if statement* one last time:

```
if (buttonPushCounter % 4 == 0) {
    digitalWrite(ledPin, HIGH);
} else {
    digitalWrite(ledPin, LOW);
}
```

If the button has been pushed 4 times, the code turns the LED on – otherwise it turns the LED off. This brings us to the end of the loop().

Let's review:

1 Check the state of the button

2 If the button state has changed...

   i If it turned on (HIGH) – increment the button counter and print some information

   ii If it turned off (LOW) – print some information

3 Update the *lastButtonState* variable with the current button state

4 Check to see if the button has been pressed 4 times…

    i   If it has – turn on the LED

    ii If it has not – turn off the LED

5 Repeat a bazillion times.

Knowing how to employ edge detection (also known as state change detection) can be useful for many applications - it doesn't just apply to pressing buttons. And while understanding the modulo operator is not essential to programming, it can be a handy tool when you need something to happen at certain intervals.

TRY ON YOUR OWN CHALLENGE:

- Can you make this program detect the falling edge? That is, the state change from HIGH to LOW?

- See if you can get another LED to turn on every 5 times the button is *released*.

FURTHER READING:

Go to the Arduino Reference webpage and read the documentation on these functions.

https://www.arduino.cc/reference/en/

- % (remainder)

Debounce a Button

KEY POINTS:

1 Button bounce happens - it won't magically leave you alone - have a plan to address it.

2 Button bounce is not due to a bad button rather to physical limitation inherent in mechanical connections.

3 Debouncing a button is one example of the usefulness of state change detection code.

In the last lesson you may have noticed that the button counts weren't exact – sometimes if you pressed the button once, it would register two or even three presses. Maybe you pressed the button four times in a row and it only registered twice. You may have wondered why that is happening.

There is a thing called bounciness – very technical I know – and it relates to the physical properties of buttons. When you press a button down, it may not immediately make a complete connection. In fact, it may make contact on one side – then both – and then the other side – until it finally settles down. This making and breaking contact is called *bouncing*. It is not a manufacturing defect of the button – bouncing is implicit in most physical switches.

Bouncing happens in a matter of milliseconds – but your microcontroller is moving so fast that it will detect a transition between two states every time the button bounces. This is why the button count from the last lesson may have been sporadic at times – it was registering unintended state changes due to bouncing.

This lesson will explore one way to "debounce" a button using code. Basically what we do is record a state change and then ignore further input for a couple milliseconds until we are satisfied the bouncing has stopped. This filters out the noise of a bouncy button.

In this example, every time you press the button, the LED will switch on or off - depending on its current state.

YOU WILL NEED:

1 LED (1)

2 10k ohm resistor (1)

3 220 ohm resistor (1)

4 Pushbutton (1)

5 Jumper wires (3)

6 Goat cheese (1 oz)

STEP-BY-STEP INSTRUCTIONS:

1 Connect an Arduino GND pin to one of the long power rails on the breadboard – this will be the ground rail.

2 Connect the short leg of the LED to the same ground rail on the breadboard and connect the long leg to a different row on the breadboard.

3 Connect the 220 ohm resistor from pin 13 to the same row where the long leg of the LED is attached.

4 Place the pushbutton on the breadboard.

5 Connect a jumper wire from the 5 volt pin to one side of the pushbutton.

6 Connect a jumper wire from pin 2 to the other side of the pushbutton.

7 Connect one side of the 10k ohm resistor to the ground rail on the breadboard and the other side to the pushbutton (on the same side that pin 2 connects).

8 Plug the Arduino board into your computer with a USB cable.

9 Open the Arduino IDE.

10 The code for this example is available on the book website.

11 Click the Verify button (check mark icon). The Arduino IDE will check your code for errors.

12 Click the Upload button (right arrow icon). You will see the TX and RX LEDs on your Arduino board begin to flash rapidly.

13 Open the serial monitor window.

14 Press the button a couple times and watch how the LED at pin 13 reacts.

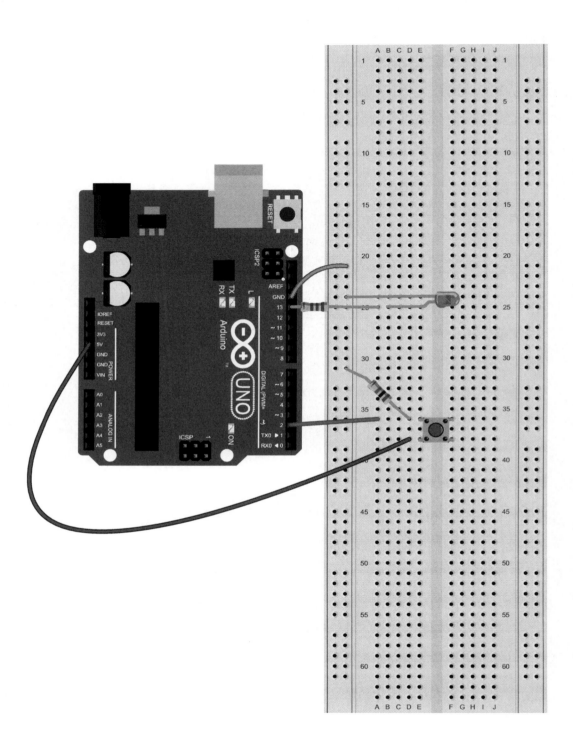

THE ARDUINO CODE:

```
/*
 * Debounce
 * Each time the input pin goes from LOW to HIGH (e.g. because
 * of a push-button press), the output pin is toggled from LOW
 * to HIGH or HIGH to LOW. There's a minimum delay between
 * toggles to debounce the circuit (i.e. to ignore noise).
 *
 * The circuit:
 * - LED attached from pin 13 to ground
 * - pushbutton attached from pin 2 to +5V
 * - 10K resistor attached from pin 2 to ground
 *
 * Note: On most Arduino boards, there is already an LED on
 * the board connected to pin 13, so you don't need any extra
 * components for this example.
 *
 * This example code is in the public domain.
 */



// Initialize and declare variables
const int ledPin = 13;     // Led attached to this pin
const int buttonPin = 2;   // Push button attached to this pin

int buttonState = LOW;
    // This variable tracks the state of the button,
    // low if not pressed, high if pressed
```

```
int ledState = -1;
    // This variable tracks the state of the LED,
    // negative if off, positive if on
long lastDebounceTime = 0;
    // The last time the output pin was toggled
long debounceDelay = 50;
    // The debounce time; increase if the output flickers


void setup() {
    // Set the mode of the pins...
    pinMode(ledPin, OUTPUT);
    pinMode(buttonPin, INPUT);
}     // Close void setup


void loop() {
    // Sample the state of the button - is it pressed or not?
    buttonState = digitalRead(buttonPin);

    // Filter out any noise by setting a time buffer
    if ((millis() - lastDebounceTime) > debounceDelay) {

        // If the button has been pressed, lets toggle the LED
        // from "off to on" or "on to off"
        if ((buttonState == HIGH) && (ledState < 0)) {

            digitalWrite(ledPin, HIGH);   // Turn LED on
            ledState = -ledState;
                // Now the LED is on, we need to change the state
            lastDebounceTime = millis();  // Set the current time
        }
```

```
    else if ((buttonState == HIGH) && (ledState > 0)) {
        digitalWrite(ledPin, LOW);      // Turn LED off
        ledState = -ledState;
            // Now the LED is off, we need to change the state
        lastDebounceTime = millis();   // Set the current time
    }  // Close if/else
  }  // Close if(time buffer)
}  // Close void loop
```

DISCUSS THE SKETCH:

This sketch is not included in the examples on your Arduino IDE. It is a slightly modified version of the Debounce sketch located in File > Examples > 02.Digital > Debounce. You can download this sketch from the book website.

We start this sketch with a handful of variables. Some variables are used to define pins:

```
const int ledPin = 13;      // Led attached to this pin
const int buttonPin = 2;    // Push button attached to this pin
```

Other variables are made to track the state of the button and the state of the LED:

```
int buttonState = LOW;
    // This variable tracks the state of the button,
    // low if not pressed, high if pressed
int ledState = -1;
    // This variable tracks the state of the LED,
    // negative if off, positive if on
```

Finally a couple *long* data type variables are initialized to keep track of time. The reason these variables are declared as *long* is because when time is measured in milliseconds the value can become a very big rather swiftly. The long data type can hold a much bigger number than an integer, making it a better suited option for these variables.

```
long lastDebounceTime = 0;
    // The last time the output pin was toggled
long debounceDelay = 50;
    // The debounce time; increase if the output flickers
```

There is a good reason for the above time tracking variables. Remember that the basis of this debounce sketch is to silence input from the pushbutton at pin 2 after the code detects a single state change. When the button is initially pressed the code registers that contact is made. The code takes this reading from pin 2, and then ignores further input until after a couple 10's of milliseconds later. It is the time tracking variables that enable this to happen.

The setup() for this sketch is rather simple, it only sets pin modes:

```
void setup() {
    // Set the mode of the pins...
    pinMode(ledPin, OUTPUT);
    pinMode(buttonPin, INPUT);
}       // Close void setup
```

The loop() is where things start to get interesting. You may have noticed that the *first thing* many sketches do inside the loop() is check the state of a pin - that way the code has the most current conditions to work with. This sketch follows the same pattern, we begin by checking the state of pin 2 to see if the button has been pressed or not:

```
// Sample the state of the button - is it pressed or not?
buttonState = digitalRead(buttonPin);
```

We use the familiar digitalRead() function which takes the pin number you want to check and returns either HIGH or LOW, based on what voltage is read at the pin. In this circuit when the pushbutton is pressed 5 volts is applied to pin 2 (HIGH), otherwise the pin is at ground voltage (LOW).

The next thing we *normally* do is test the value we just sampled against a condition – in this example however, we want to check how much time has passed between collecting the current sample and when we received the last sample. If the new sample came in just 1 millisecond after the last sample – we will ignore it. If it came in 2 milliseconds after the last sample, we will ignore it too. In fact, we only want to accept a sample that was taken at least 50 milliseconds after the last sample. How do we implement this as a condition? We use the microcontrollers internal clock with the function millis():

```
if ((millis() - lastDebounceTime) > debounceDelay)
```

The above condition takes the current time and subtracts it from the last time a legitimate input was received, it then checks if the span of time is greater then a preset threshold which is named *debounceDelay*. It basically says, "Has enough time passed for me to even consider a new input?"

This is the gate, the filter, that blocks the noise of a bouncing button. Once we know a reasonable amount of time has passed, we will accept the input and begin to process it.

We use an *if-else statement* to do more filtering:

```
if ((buttonState == HIGH) && (ledState < 0)) {
    digitalWrite(ledPin, HIGH);    // Turn LED on
    ledState = -ledState;
        // Now the LED is on, we need to change the state
    lastDebounceTime = millis();   // Set the current time
}
```

We are only interested when the LED goes from LOW to HIGH, this is the rising edge of the input. *Pressing* the button initiates the *rising edge*. *Releasing* the button initiates the *falling edge*.

The *if statement* checks these two conditions:

1. That the input from pin 2 is HIGH

2. That the *ledState* variable is less than zero (The LED is off - more on this in a moment)

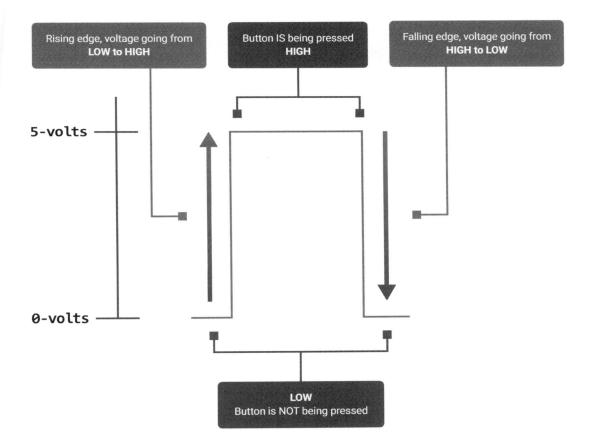

You can see that we have multiple conditions that must be met – we use two ampersands (&&) to join these two conditions together:

```
if ((buttonState == HIGH) && (ledState < 0))
```

This condition asks, "Is the button pressed *and* is the LED off?" If yes, execute the code inside the *if statement*. If one of these conditions is not met, the code inside the *if statement* is skipped. Both conditions must be met for the *if statement* to execute.

If the condition of the if statement is met, we do three things:

1. Turn the LED on

2. Update the state of the LED from off to on

3. Update the *lastDebounceTime* variable

```
if ((buttonState == HIGH) && (ledState < 0)) {
    digitalWrite(ledPin, HIGH);    // Turn LED on
    ledState = -ledState;
        // Now the LED is on, we need to change the state
    lastDebounceTime = millis();   // Set the current time
}
```

Let's discuss the code block above line-by-line. First, we turn on the LED by using digitalWrite() to apply high voltage to pin 13. Second, we multiply the *ledState* variable by a negative one (-1) to change its sign from negative to positive. For our purposes, if the *ledState* variable is negative it means the LED is off, and if *ledState* is positive the LED is on. Finally, we update the *lastDebounceTime* to the current time using the millis() function again.

Now when button is released the LED will stay on – all we did was toggle the LED from off to on with a button press. What happens when we press the button again? Ideally, the LED turns off.

To turn off the LED we once again refer to the rising edge of the input. We want to know when the button is pressed again – but this time we want to address the scenario when the button is pressed *and* the LED is already on. The next part of the code addresses this condition:

```
else if ((buttonState == HIGH) && (ledState > 0)) {
    digitalWrite(ledPin, LOW);      // Turn LED off
    ledState = -ledState;
        // Now the LED is off, we need to change the state
    lastDebounceTime = millis();  // Set the current time
}  // Close if/else
```

The condition of the *else-if statement* requires *buttonState* to be HIGH and *ledState* to be positive (on). Inside this statement, we toggle the LED off by writing digital pin 13 LOW.

A little caveat:

Notice how the *if-else statement* has multiple conditions. The general form of these *if-else statements* is as follows:

```
if (condition) {
    Do something;
} else if (condition) {
    Do something else;
} else if (condition) {
    Do something else;
} else {
    Do this if no condition is met;

}
```

In the example sketch we have been using, we do not have a final *else statement* that is a catchall – we set very specific conditions and we only want to act on those conditions. In this way we ignore the input that comes from the falling edge - when the button is released and the voltage at pin 2 changes from HIGH to LOW.

The very next time through the loop() we read the voltage at the button again, but that reading (and following readings) are filtered by the debounce *if-statement* condition until we reach the time threshold previously set.

If you still have bouncing issues with the button, try increasing the *debounceDelay* variable from 50 to 100. This increase will ignore input even longer, but there is a price to pay. What if someone wants to rapidly toggle the LED by pressing the button very fast? This is a circumstance when you will run into trouble if you make the *debounceDelay* too long. If you are making a video game controller this could be a definite issue!

TRY ON YOUR OWN CHALLENGE:

- Try increasing and decreasing the *debounceDelay* time and observe the effect.

- Add an LED to pin 12 and change the code so that every time you press the button the LEDs toggle between each other (i.e., one is on when the other is off).

FURTHER READING:

Go to the Arduino Reference webpage and read the documentation on these functions.

https://www.arduino.cc/reference/en/

- ! (logical not)
- && (logical and)
- || (logical or)

CHAPTER

05

ANALOG

The world is analog. It is a continuous stream of data waiting to be collected and processed. You will frequently find yourself converting this rich analog world into convenient digital output. This chapter seeks to illuminate some options for this procedure and add to your growing repertoire of functions.

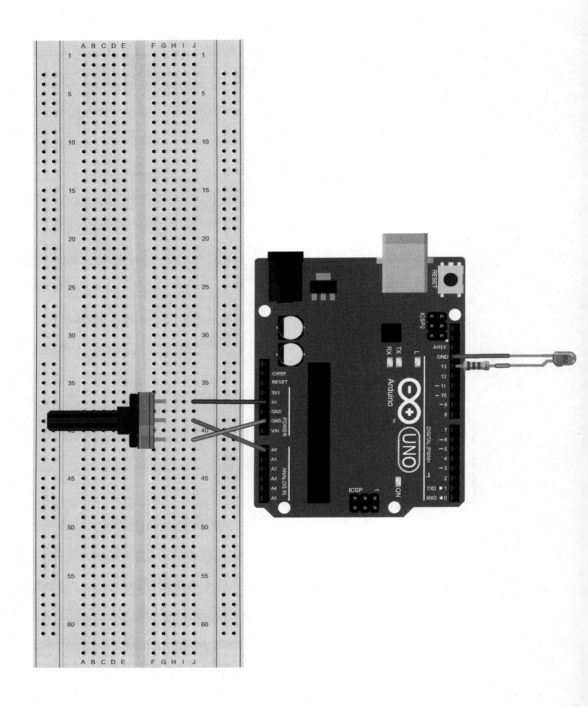

Analog Input/Output

KEY POINTS:

1   Analog inputs are frequently converted to digital outputs.

2   Mapping an analog input to a set of digital outputs is like assigning the broad spectrum of a rainbow to a specific set of crayons. Fewer crayons result in decreased resolution.

I often wonder who would win if Frankenstein's monster and Dracula got into a fight. My personal bet is on the monster – but I would be concerned with Dracula doing some funky vampire mind control trick.

Now this lesson doesn't use mind control, but it does use an analog input to control the output of a digital pin. Controlling a digital pin with an analog input can be extremely helpful because many sensors report analog data.

This lesson explores how to use analog input to adjust the intensity of an LED.

YOU WILL NEED:

1 LED (1)

2 220 ohm resistor (1)

3 Potentiometer (1) - Any resistance is fine.

4 Jumper wires (3)

5 Alligator clip (1)

6 Juice mix (12 ounce)

STEP-BY-STEP INSTRUCTIONS:

1 Place the potentiometer into the breadboard pictured in the circuit diagram.

2 Run a jumper wire from the 5 volt pin of the Arduino to either one of the outside pins of the potentiometer.

3 Run another jumper wire from one of the ground pins on the Arduino (labeled GND) to the other outside pin of the potentiometer.

4 Run the final jumper wire from pin A0 on the Arduino to the middle pin of the potentiometer.

5 Place one end of the 220 ohm resistor into pin 9.

6 Place the short leg of the LED into the ground pin next to pin 13.

7 Connect the long leg of the LED to the other end of the resistor with the alligator clip.

8 Plug the Arduino into your computer.

9 Open the Arduino IDE.

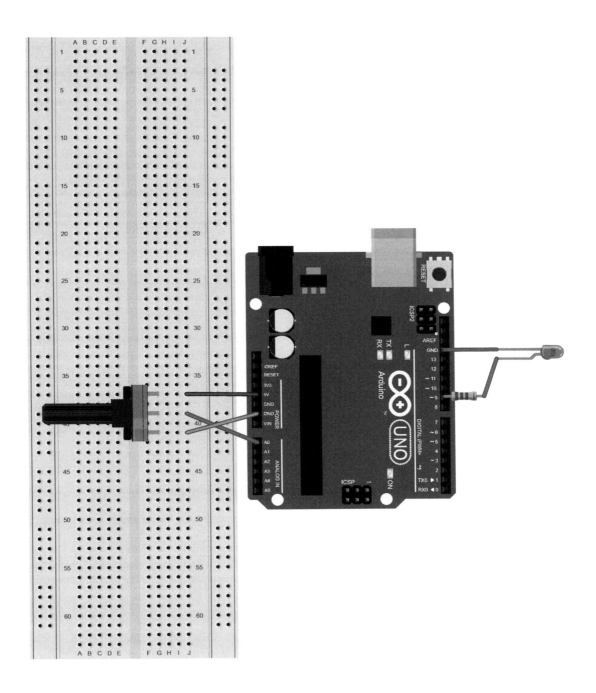

(10) Open the sketch for this section.

(11) Click the Verify button (check mark icon). The Arduino IDE will check your code for errors.

(12) Click the Upload button (right arrow icon). You will see the TX and RX LEDs on your Arduino board begin to flash rapidly.

(13) Open the serial monitor window – sensor input and output data should be streaming along.

(14) As you adjust the knob of the potentiometer the brightness of the LED should vary.

THE ARDUINO CODE:

```
/*
 * Analog input, analog output, serial output
 * Reads an analog input pin, maps the result to a range
 * from 0 to 255 and uses the result to set the pulsewidth
 * modulation (PWM) of an output pin. Also prints the results
 * to the serial monitor.
 *
 * The circuit:
 * - potentiometer connected to analog pin 0.
 * - Center pin of the potentiometer goes to the analog pin.
 * - Side pins of the potentiometer go to +5V and ground
 * - LED connected from digital pin 9 to ground
 *
 * This example code is in the public domain.
 */
```

```
// These constants won't change. They're used to give names
// to the pins used:
const int analogInPin = A0;
    // Analog input pin that the potentiometer is attached to
const int analogOutPin = 9;
    // Analog output pin that the LED is attached to

int sensorValue = 0;    // Value read from the pot
int outputValue = 0;    // Value output to the PWM (analog out)



void setup() {
    // Initialize serial communications at 9600 bps:
    Serial.begin(9600);
}



void loop() {
    // Read the analog in value:
    sensorValue = analogRead(analogInPin);
    // Map it to the range of the analog out:
    outputValue = map(sensorValue, 0, 1023, 0, 255);
    // Change the analog out value:
    analogWrite(analogOutPin, outputValue);

    // Print the results to the serial monitor:
    Serial.print("sensor = " );
    Serial.print(sensorValue);
    Serial.print("\t output = ");
    Serial.println(outputValue);
```

```
// Wait 2 milliseconds before the next loop
// for the analog-to-digital converter to settle
// after the last reading:
delay(2);
}
```

DISCUSS THE SKETCH:

This sketch begins by declaring and initializing two variables, one for the potentiometer input pin and one for the LED output pin. The variables are qualified as *constants* which keeps them safe from being changed anywhere else in the program:

```
const int analogInPin = A0;
    // Analog input pin that the potentiometer is attached to
const int analogOutPin = 9;
    // Analog output pin that the LED is attached to
```

The next variables created are *integers* used for storing input and output data:

```
int sensorValue = 0;     // Value read from the pot
int outputValue = 0;     // Value output to the PWM (analog out)
```

The setup() of this function is simple, we initiate serial communications with the Serial.begin() function:

```
void setup() {
    // Initialize serial communications at 9600 bps:
    Serial.begin(9600);
}
```

Now we proceed to the last block of code, the loop().

The loop() first reads the value at analog pin A0 (where the potentiometer is attached) and assigns this value to a variable named *sensorValue*:

```
// Read the analog in value:
sensorValue = analogRead(analogInPin);
```

Recall that analogRead() returns a value between 0 and 1023. In this example we use the input value we just recorded as the output value for the analogWrite() function. But wait a minute! The analogWrite() function will only accept values in the range of 0 through 255...the value we record with analogRead() can be much larger.

One solution to this problem is to rescale the input values to within the range of the analogWrite() function. The map() function does this easily:

```
// Map it to the range of the analog out:
outputValue = map(sensorValue, 0, 1023, 0, 255);
```

Recall that map() takes 5 arguments:

```
map(Variable_to_be_Mapped, Low_Range, High_Range, New_Low, New_High)
```

In this case we use the map() function to adjust the input value to correspond with the range of analogWrite(). Now that we have a value that will work with analogWrite(), let's go ahead and get started with the output:

```
analogWrite(analogOutPin, outputValue);
```

As you may recall, analogWrite() takes two arguments 1) a pin number 2) the value to write. This function utilizes pulse width modulation, allowing you to adjust the power output of the PWM enabled pin (in this case pin 9 where we have the LED attached).

Recapping what we have done:

1 Read the input from analog pin A0

2 Adjusted the value to a condensed range using the map() function

3 Passed the value to analogWrite() which in turn adjusts the brightness of the LED

Pretty simple - highly useful.

But what is a program without some type of data output? We get our fix by writing the input and output values to the serial port.

```
// Print the results to the serial monitor:
Serial.print("sensor = " );
Serial.print(sensorValue);
Serial.print("\t output = ");
Serial.println(outputValue);
```

The \t in the third statement will insert a {TAB} into the string. Notice how the last Serial.println() function is different - it has "println" instead of just "print". The println() function prints the *outputValue* variable and then starts a *newline* in the serial monitor window - this way all the information lines up nicely. A *newline* is like pressing the return key in a word editing program - it moves to the next line.

The last line of the sketch is the delay() function, which allows the analog-to-digital converter to stabilize before we feed it another input at the top of the loop().

Let's review what this loop() does:

1 Reads an input value at analog pin A0

2 Assigns the value to a variable

3 Changes the input value to match the scale of the output's allowable range

4 Assigns the new mapped value to a variable

5 Feeds the variable to analogWrite() to adjust the brightness of an LED

6 Delays the program for 2 milliseconds to ensure the next reading is stable

TRY ON YOUR OWN CHALLENGE:

- Instead of having the potentiometer adjust the brightness of the LED at pin 9, can you make it adjust the rate at which it blinks?

- Can you add another LED at pin 11, and have that LED get bright, while the LED at pin 9 goes dark as you adjust the potentiometer?

FURTHER READING:

Go to the Arduino Reference webpage and read the documentation on these functions.

https://www.arduino.cc/reference/en/

- map()

Analog Input

KEY POINTS:

1   With microcontrollers, you generally sample sensors at timed intervals, then perform an action based on the data collected. How often you sample is a decision based on the design requirements.

2   Timing of events in projects is critical, think of the "time-domain" as a space that you can and should control.

Using a microcontroller can be a lot like fishing – you throw your sensor out in the world and then check your line every so often. Sometimes you get just the fish you are looking for – but what will you do with it once you have it? Will you keep it or release it? Will you pan fry it or eat some sashimi?

The same questions are involved in the data you capture with your microcontroller. What will you do with the data once you have it?

In the last lesson we used input data to control the *intensity* of an output, in this example will use the input data to control the *timing* of an output.

To demonstrate this, we use a potentiometer attached to analog pin A0 and an LED attached to digital pin 13. We use the input from the analog pin to adjust the timing delay of a blinking LED.

YOU WILL NEED:

1 LED (1)

2 220 ohm resistor (1)

3 Potentiometer (1) - Any resistance is fine.

4 Jumper wires (3)

5 Alligator clip (1)

6 Jar of elbow grease (1)

STEP-BY-STEP INSTRUCTIONS:

1 Place the potentiometer into the breadboard.

2 Run a jumper wire from the 5 volt pin of the Arduino to either one of the outside pins of the potentiometer.

3 Run another jumper wire from one of the ground pins on the Arduino (labeled GND), to the other outside pin of the potentiometer.

4 Run the final jumper wire from pin A0 on the Arduino to the middle pin of the potentiometer.

5 Place one end of the 220 ohm resistor into pin 13.

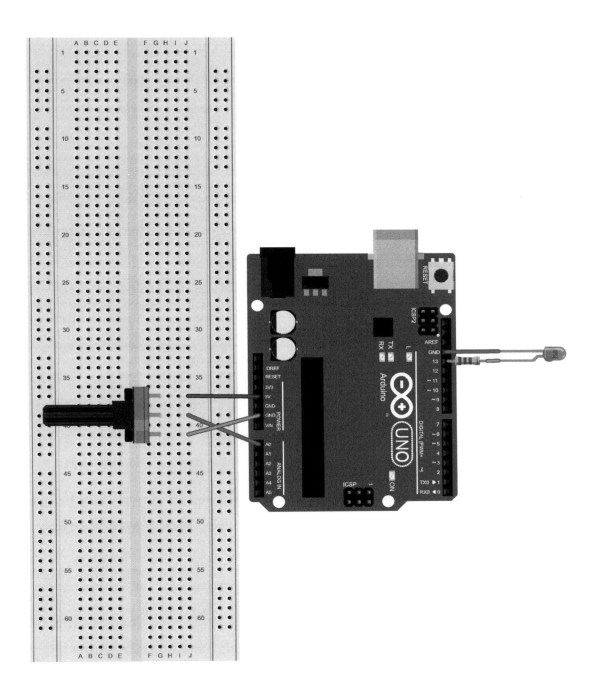

6 Place the short leg of the LED into the ground pin.

7 Connect the long leg of the LED to the other end of the resistor with the alligator clip.

8 Plug the Arduino into your computer.

9 Open the Arduino IDE.

10 Open the sketch for this section.

11 Click the Verify button (check mark icon). The Arduino IDE will check your code for errors.

12 Click the Upload button (right arrow icon). You will see the TX and RX LEDs on your Arduino board begin to flash rapidly.

13 Now adjust the knob of the potentiometer and watch the LED. The knob should adjust the on/off timing of the LED.

THE ARDUINO CODE:

```
/*
* Analog Input
* Demonstrates analog input by reading an analog sensor
* on analog pin 0 and turning on and off a light emitting
* diode(LED) connected to digital pin 13.
* The amount of time the LED will be on and off depends
* on the value obtained by analogRead().
*
* The circuit:
* - Potentiometer attached to analog input 0
* - center pin of the potentiometer to the analog pin
```

```
* - one side pin (either one) to ground
* - the other side pin to +5V
* - LED anode (long leg) attached to digital output 13
* - LED cathode (short leg) attached to ground
*
* Note: because most Arduinos have a built-in LED attached
* to pin 13 on the board, the LED is optional.
*
* This example code is in the public domain.
*/


int sensorPin = A0;
    // Select the input pin for the potentiometer
int ledPin = 13;
    // Select the pin for the LED
int sensorValue = 0;
    // Variable to store the value coming from the sensor


void setup() {
    // Declare the ledPin as an OUTPUT:
    pinMode(ledPin, OUTPUT);
}


void loop() {
    // Read the value from the sensor:
    sensorValue = analogRead(sensorPin);
    // Turn the ledPin on
    digitalWrite(ledPin, HIGH);
```

```
// Stop the program for <sensorValue> milliseconds:
delay(sensorValue);
// Turn the ledPin off:
digitalWrite(ledPin, LOW);
// Stop the program for for <sensorValue> milliseconds:
delay(sensorValue);
}
```

DISCUSS THE SKETCH:

This sketch is fun and easy, but at the same time helps you think of creative ways to use an analog input. First we declare and initialize variables for two pins and a variable to hold the data we collect from the sensor (i.e., in this case, the potentiometer is our "sensor"):

```
int sensorPin = A0;
    // Select the input pin for the potentiometer
int ledPin = 13;
    // Select the pin for the LED
int sensorValue = 0;
    // Variable to store the value coming from the sensor
```

All the variables are simple integers. Note that the programmer chose not to use the constant qualifier for these pin assignments – it is by no means a requirement, but it is a good practice.

In the setup() of this sketch we need to make sure the pin used to brighten the LED is set as an output:

```
void setup() {
    // Declare the ledPin as an OUTPUT:
    pinMode(ledPin, OUTPUT);
}
```

Once the setup() is complete we begin with the loop(). This loop() is rather easy. We start by collecting a sample from the analog pin using the analogRead() function. We assign the value we get from analogRead() to the *sensorValue* variable.

```
// Read the value from the sensor:
sensorValue = analogRead(sensorPin);
```

Because we want the LED to blink we need to turn it on, to do that all we need is to write the pin as HIGH:

```
// Turn the ledPin on:
digitalWrite(ledPin, HIGH);
```

This applies 5 volts to pin 13, allowing current to flow through the LED which turns it on. Now comes the timing control piece – we want the input from the analog pin to determine the interval the LED stays on and off.

To do this, we delay() the sketch using the *sensorValue* variable:

```
// Stop the program for <sensorValue> milliseconds:
delay(sensorValue);
```

Now the LED is bright for the number of milliseconds that corresponds to the potentiometer's adjustment. Recall that the highest value which analogRead() returns is 1023 and the lowest is 0. There are a thousand milliseconds in a second, therefore, the longest amount of time the LED will be lit is slightly over one second.

The next logical step is to have the LED turn off – we are trying to blink it after all – again we employ the digitalWrite() function, but set the voltage LOW:

```
// Turn the ledPin off:
digitalWrite(ledPin, LOW);
```

The final step in the program is to hold the LED in the off state for the same period it was on. We pull out the delay() function again and feed it the same sensor value as before:

```
// Stop the program for for <sensorValue> milliseconds:
delay(sensorValue);
```

Once the loop() finishes it starts at the top and goes over and over. Here are the basic steps of the program:

1 Sample data at the analog pin and assign it to a variable

2 Turn the LED on

3 Delay the sketch for a specified time

4 Turn the LED off

5 Delay the sketch for the same specified time

Keep in mind that since we employ the delay() function to control the timing, all the input coming from the potentiometer is halted while the sketch is delayed.

TRY ON YOUR OWN CHALLENGE:

- Adjust the delay time so that the LED off interval is half that of the LED on interval.

- Add an LED at pin 12 and make it blink the exact opposite as the LED at pin 13.

Calibration

KEY POINTS:

1   Training your sensor to a specific environment will reduce the collection of unwanted information.

2   Using LEDs as indicator lights is extremely useful when developing code. Don't be afraid to have an LED blink a special way as a tool to test the functionality of code.

3   The *while statement* only gets executed when a specific condition is met - but once it starts it won't stop until the condition ceases to be true.

The world is a busy place. Sometimes in order to get the right kind of information you need to block out all the noise and focus on just one thing or a small range of things. This focusing process is a form of calibration.

In this example you calibrate a sensor by exposing it in the first 5 seconds of the sketch to the highest and lowest inputs that you want monitored. You are basically *tuning* the sensor.

We do this by adjusting the position of the potentiometer knob for five seconds when the program is initiated. The code inside the setup() encodes the highest and the lowest voltages that occur during this calibration period. These minimum and maximum values are used for the remainder of the sketch to map sensor readings to a new range. Basically, the sketch ignores any input higher or lower than the initial readings. These mapped inputs are used to set the brightness of an LED.

Why do this? Wouldn't it make more sense to use the full range of the sensor? Good question.

Think for a moment about how your microcontroller records inputs at an analog pin. If there is 0 voltage at the pin, the microcontroller returns 0 with the analogRead() function. If 5 volts are at the analog pin, then analogRead() reports 1023.

So if you want the full scale at the analog pin you need a sensor that will vary from 0 to 5 volts. Even if your sensor is capable of a 5 volt swing, what if the inputs required to get the 5 volt swing are out of the range for your application.

Take for example a light sensor in a dark cave that must monitor light levels produced by the flashlights of miners passing by. The sensor sends a signal to a computer station and says on a scale from dark to bright how much light is being produced, with dark being pitch black and bright being a fully charged flashlight. A fully charged flashlight might not be bright enough to make your sensor change voltage at a range from 0 to 5 volts – maybe it is more like 0 to 3 volts (though one might argue you need a differ- ent light sensor). When you read the voltage at the analog pin, there will be lots of unused range – which is fine, but you want to make sure your program lets the computer station know that a change of 3 volts is full bright.

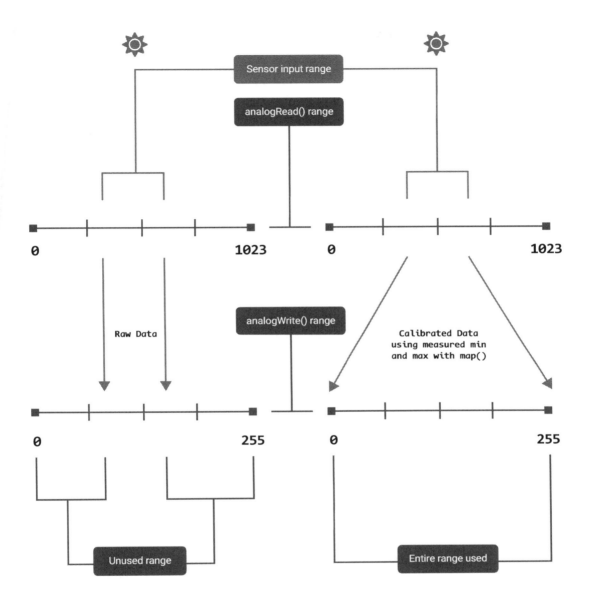

Another example where this type of calibration makes sense is when any input higher than a certain level will automatically be the highest you care to know about.

Say you have a light sensor attached to a widget, and when the light in a room is turned on, then you want the widget to do something. There is no need to monitor levels of ambient light brighter than what your sensor will experience when the light is on – so whatever reading you get when someone shines a bright flash light directly at your sensor will be bound by the maximum the sensor would experience with the room light turned on. Note that this does not prevent the widget from "thinking" that the light is on, but it confines the input to within the range you programmed it to handle.

A more abstract way to think about this is imagining a curved grade on a college exam. For example, pretend an exam has 100 questions, but the highest scoring student only answers 88 questions correct. A professor may curve the scoring so that the new 100% score is equivalent to having 88 questions correct.

As you work through this program I am sure you will think of many other ways to accomplish a task like this. This lesson is meant to stimulate thinking about sensor ranges, and what ranges are important to you and how to focus on the ranges that will be most useful for your application.

YOU WILL NEED:

1. LED (1)

2. 220 ohm resistor (1)

3. Potentiometer (1) - Any resistance is fine.

4. Jumper wires (3)

5. Alligator clip (1)

6. Another jar of elbow grease (1)

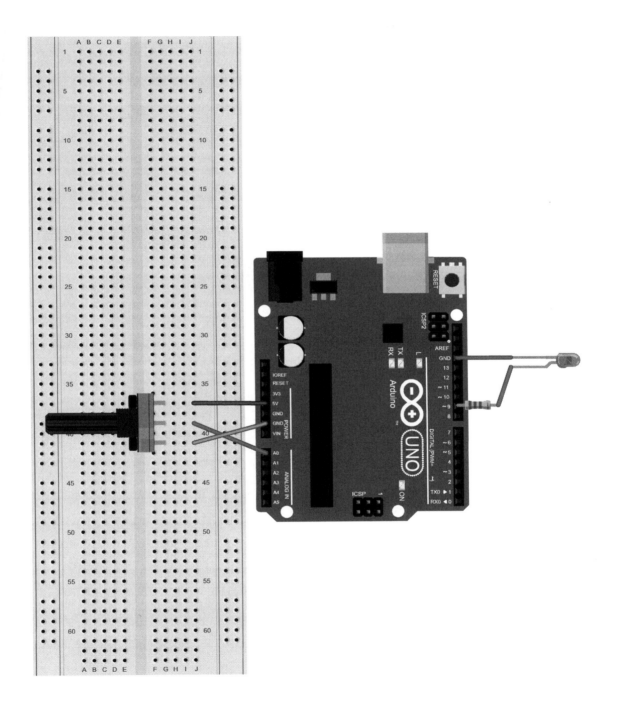

STEP-BY-STEP INSTRUCTIONS:

1 Place the potentiometer into the breadboard.

2 Run a jumper wire from the 5 volt pin of the Arduino to either one of the outside pins of the potentiometer.

3 Run another jumper wire from one of the ground pins on the Arduino (labeled GND) to the other outside pin of the potentiometer.

4 Run the final jumper wire from pin A0 on the Arduino to the middle pin of the potentiometer.

5 Place one end of the 220 ohm resistor into pin 9.

6 Place the short leg of the LED into the ground pin.

7 Connect the long leg of the LED to the other end of the resistor with the alligator clip.

8 Plug the Arduino into your computer.

9 Open up the Arduino IDE.

10 Open the sketch for this section.

11 Click the Verify button (check mark icon). The Arduino IDE will check your code for errors.

12 Click the Upload button (right arrow icon). You will see the TX and RX LEDs on your Arduino board begin to flash rapidly.

13 Immediately after uploading the sketch, wait for the LED at pin 13 to turn on. Once it does, adjust the knob of the potentiometer back and forth, but not full scale. This is the calibration period, where the highest and lowest values are being recorded.

14 After the LED at pin 13 turns off, adjust your potentiometer. Even though you don't turn the knob full scale, the LED will still go from full dark to full bright.

THE ARDUINO CODE:

```
/*
 * Calibration
 * Demonstrates one technique for calibrating sensor input.
 * The sensor readings during the first five seconds of the
   sketch
 * execution define the minimum and maximum of expected values
 * attached to the sensor pin. The sensor minimum and maximum
 * initial values may seem backwards. Initially, you set the
 * minimum high and listen for anything lower, saving it as the
 * new minimum. Likewise, you set the maximum low and listen
 * for anything higher as the new maximum.
 *
 * The circuit:
 * - Analog sensor (potentiometer will do) attached to analog
 *    input 0
 * - LED attached from digital pin 9 to ground
 *
 * This example code is in the public domain.
 */



// These constants won't change:
const int sensorPin = A0;  // Pin that the sensor is attached to
const int ledPin = 9;      // Pin that the LED is attached to

// Variables:
int sensorValue = 0;       // The sensor value
int sensorMin = 1023;      // Minimum sensor value
int sensorMax = 0;         // Maximum sensor value
```

```
void setup() {
    // Turn on LED to signal the start of the calibration period:
    pinMode(13, OUTPUT);
    digitalWrite(13, HIGH);

    // Calibrate during the first five seconds
    while (millis() < 5000) {
        sensorValue = analogRead(sensorPin);

        // Record the maximum sensor value
        if (sensorValue > sensorMax) {
            sensorMax = sensorValue;
        }

        // Record the minimum sensor value
        if (sensorValue < sensorMin) {
            sensorMin = sensorValue;
        }
    }

// Signal the end of the calibration period
digitalWrite(13, LOW);
}


void loop() {
    // Read the sensor:
    sensorValue = analogRead(sensorPin);

    // Apply the calibration to the sensor reading
    sensorValue = map(sensorValue, sensorMin, sensorMax, 0, 255);
```

```
    // In case the sensor value is outside the range seen
    // during calibration
    sensorValue = constrain(sensorValue, 0, 255);

    // Fade the LED using the calibrated value:
    analogWrite(ledPin, sensorValue);
}
```

DISCUSS THE SKETCH:

This program begins by declaring and initializing a couple Arduino pins and setting them as constants. The other variables it creates will be used to store the highest and lowest sensor value ranges:

```
// These constants won't change:
const int sensorPin = A0;  // Pin that the sensor is attached to
const int ledPin = 9;      // Pin that the LED is attached to

// Variables:
int sensorValue = 0;       // The sensor value
int sensorMin = 1023;      // Minimum sensor value
int sensorMax = 0;         // Maximum sensor value
```

This programmer made very descriptive and logical names for the variables – this is something we should all aspire to.

The setup() in this function is where the business of calibrating our sensor happens. While we are not accustomed to running much code in setup(), we must consider that the calibration process will only occur once at the beginning of the program - making the setup() the ideal location.

The first thing we do is to let the user know "Hey – I am in calibration mode!" – a simple way to do this is to turn on an LED:

```
// Turn on LED to signal the start of the calibration period:
pinMode(13, OUTPUT);
digitalWrite(13, HIGH);
```

Next we start taking readings for five seconds and record the highest and lowest values. Why five seconds? It is just an arbitrary number the programmer used – it could be any length you desire. An easy way to implement a five second window is using the *while statement*.

Think of the *while statement* just like a *for loop*. A *for loop* continues over and over until a certain condition is met and increments a counter along the way. The *while statement* also continues over and over, but does not have a built in counter – it uses an "outside" condition to stop it. Let's take a close look at the condition in this *while statement*:

```
while (millis() < 5000)
```

Recall that the millis() function returns in milliseconds the elapsed time from when the program first began. This condition ensures that the elapsed time is less than 5000 milliseconds. In the first five seconds all the code following the curly brackets of the *while statement* is executed – but as soon as five seconds has passed, the condition will no longer be true and the program moves to the next block of code.

So what code is running during the first five seconds?

```
// Calibrate during the first five seconds
while (millis() < 5000) {
    sensorValue = analogRead(sensorPin);

    // Record the maximum sensor value
    if (sensorValue > sensorMax) {
        sensorMax = sensorValue;
    }
    // Record the minimum sensor value
    if (sensorValue < sensorMin) {
        sensorMin = sensorValue;
    }
}
```

The first thing to do is record the current sensor value using analogRead(), and assign it to a variable called *sensorValue*:

```
sensorValue = analogRead(sensorPin);
```

Nothing new here – you are accustomed to recording sensor values.

Next we want to check if this is the highest value we have recorded thus far. Keep in mind that when this code is running, the user is adjusting the input to the sensor. In our case we are simulating a sensor by adjusting the potentiometer a little bit, but it just as well could be a sensor registering ambient light levels or fluctuating temperatures. We use an *if statement* to capture the highest input:

```
// Record the maximum sensor value
if (sensorValue > sensorMax) {
    sensorMax = sensorValue;
}
```

Here the condition asks "Is the current sensor reading greater than the last sensor reading?" If this is the case, we assign the current sensor reading to the *sensorMax* variable. This process ensures that the greatest sensor reading encountered during the calibration process is set as the upper range.

The next *if statement* does the same thing, but it looks for the lowest sensor reading:

```
// Record the minimum sensor value
if (sensorValue < sensorMin) {
    sensorMin = sensorValue;
}
```

Here the condition asks "Is the current sensor reading less than the lowest sensor reading?" If yes, assign the current sensor reading to the *sensorMin* variable. This process ensures that the lowest sensor reading encountered during the calibration process is set as the lower range.

This will happen over and over for five seconds, when all is said and done, you will have a new *sensorMin* and *sensorMax* value to work with for the duration of the sketch.

Now that the calibration is complete we need notify the user - let's turn off the LED:

```
// Signal the end of the calibration period
digitalWrite(13, LOW);
```

This completes the setup() portion of the program. A lot takes place in this setup() – which is unusual compared to what we typically see, but makes perfect sense for this application.

Now me move on to the loop(). The first thing to do is measure the voltage at analog pin 0:

```
// Read the sensor:
sensorValue = analogRead(sensorPin);
```

Once the measurement is taken, it's mapped to the calibrated range that was established in setup(). The map() function is used to accomplish this:

```
// Apply the calibration to the sensor reading
sensorValue = map(sensorValue, sensorMin, sensorMax, 0, 255);
```

But what happens if the sensor records an input outside the range of *sensorMin* and *sensorMax* that was established during the setup()? To be clear – let's say the maximum value we recorded at the analog pin was 500 and the minimum value was 150. What will happen if a reading of 728 is encountered? That is way over the maximum range!

The reason for the calibration process is to focus our sensor on a specific range of inputs, therefore we must guard against readings that deviate from this scale of interest. To do this we use the *constrain()* function:

Constrain() caps the value high or low

```
sensorValue = 10;
sensorValue = constrain(sensorValue, 100, 300);
                                     VALUE      MIN   MAX

                sensorValue now equals 100
```

```
sensorValue = 400;
sensorValue = constrain(sensorValue, 100, 300);
                       VALUE          MIN   MAX
```

sensorValue now equals 300

```
sensorValue = constrain(sensorValue, 0, 255);
```

The constrain() function takes three arguments 1) the value in question 2) a lowValue 3) a highValue. If the value in question is larger than the highValue, constrain() will return the highValue – capping the size. Likewise, if the value in question is lower then the lowValue, constrain will return the lowValue – capping the low end.

In the setup(), the input was focused on a specific range. In the loop(), we make sure any outliers of that range are capped at the specified maximum and minimum values. This completes our calibration.

Now let's use the calibrated data to adjust an output. We use analogWrite() to set the brightness of an LED attached to pin 9:

```
// Fade the LED using the calibrated value:
analogWrite(ledPin, sensorValue);
```

A recap of this program:

1 For five seconds measure a sensor for a low and high value to establish a desired range.

2 Use this range to map future sensor inputs.

3 Constrain the mapped values to the previously established min and max.

4 Adjust an LED based on the mapped and constrained values.

5 Repeat till the cows come home.

TRY ON YOUR OWN CHALLENGE:

• Write a program that allows you to press a pushbutton in order to restart the calibration process. You will need to move the calibration code from the setup() to the loop().

FURTHER READING:

Go to the Arduino Reference webpage and read the documentation on these functions.

https://www.arduino.cc/reference/en/

• while

• constrain()

Smoothing Data

> **KEY POINTS:**
>
> 1   Smoothing data takes out the big spikes and valleys that may not represent the "big picture" of sensor information.
>
> 2   The more you smooth data, the less detailed it becomes - be careful not to over smooth.
>
> 3   An array is a useful data structure for storing information that needs processed.

Have you ever sat down and tried to figure out your finances and come up with a budget? Let's say you're looking at last year's expenditures and determine that you spent $642 of your hard earned cash on ice cream and tacos – that's roughly $53 dollars per month.

Even though one month you might have spent $75 and the next month only $30, the average over the year gives you the "big picture" of what you spent overall. This average is useful to help determine the budget for those items next year.

Sometimes sensor data varies like this too. One reading is 75 and the next is 30, but if you average the inputs over time you get a number that falls around 53. This variability may be due to a rapidly changing environment or an imprecise sensor. Since Arduino can sample sensors super fast – hundreds of times a second – averaging inputs can help smooth this variability.

Smoothed output is helpful when you are collecting trend data i.e., "Is a value increasing or decreasing over time?"

Smoothed data creates a more stable output. Suppose you are using the input to position a servo motor – controlling its movement with smoothed data keeps it fluid – not jumpy.

There is a trade off here of course, the more you smooth the data the less detailed it becomes. If you smooth too much, instead of getting accurate information you may eliminate the useful variability you are trying to capture. It's a lot about trial and error. What works with the given set of restrictions you have? The degree of smoothing necessary will vary with each application.

To help us smooth inputs we revisit an awesome data structure – the array. As you may recall, an array is simply a list of items. The array is useful for smoothing data because we can store multiple sensor readings in an array and then perform simple arithmetic to calculate an average.

YOU WILL NEED:

1. Potentiometer (1) - Any resistance is fine.

2. Jumper wires (3)

3. Goldfinch (1) - European variety.

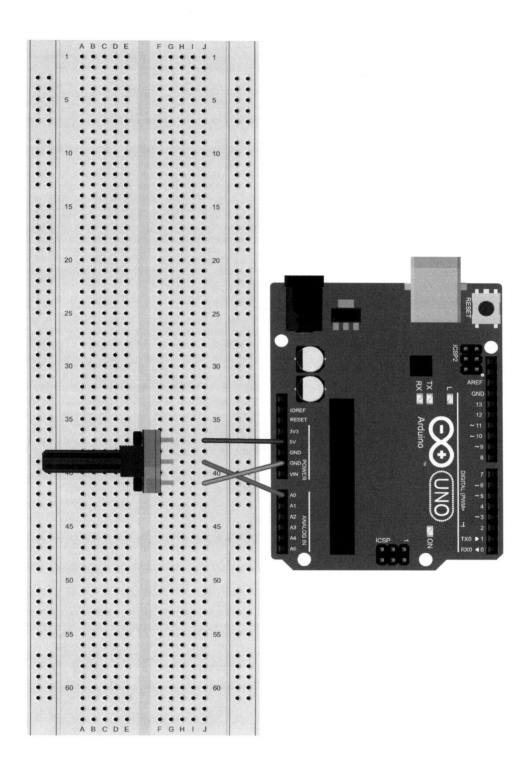

STEP-BY-STEP INSTRUCTIONS:

1 Place the potentiometer into the breadboard.

2 Run a jumper wire from the 5V pin of the Arduino to either one of the outside pins of your potentiometer.

3 Run another jumper wire from one of the ground pins on the Arduino (labeled GND) to the other outside pin of the potentiometer.

4 Run the final jumper wire from pin A0 on the Arduino to the middle pin of the potentiometer.

5 Plug the Arduino into your computer.

6 Open up the Arduino IDE.

7 Open the sketch for this section.

8 Click the Verify button (check mark icon). The Arduino IDE will check your code for errors.

9 Click the Upload button (right arrow icon). You will see the TX and RX LEDs on your Arduino board begin to flash rapidly.

10 Open the Serial Monitor window.

11 Adjust the knob of the potentiometer and see the resulting smoothed data on the Serial Monitor window.

THE ARDUINO CODE:

```
/*
 * Smoothing
 *
```

```
 * Reads repeatedly from an analog input, calculating a running
 * average and printing it to the computer. Keeps ten readings
 * in an array and continually averages them.
 *
 * The circuit:
 * - Analog sensor (potentiometer will do) attached to
 *   analog input 0
 *
 * This example code is in the public domain.
 */


// Define the number of samples to keep track of. The higher
// the number, the more the readings will be smoothed, but
// the slower the output will respond to the input. Using a
// constant rather than a normal variable lets use this value
// to determine the size of the readings array.


const int numReadings = 10;

int readings[numReadings]; // The readings from the analog input
int index = 0;             // The index of the current reading
int total = 0;             // The running total
int average = 0;           // The average
int inputPin = A0;


void setup() {
    // Initialize serial communication with computer:
    Serial.begin(9600);
```

```
    // Initialize all the readings to 0:
    for (int thisReading = 0; thisReading < numReadings;
        thisReading++) {
        readings[thisReading] = 0;
    }
}


void loop() {
    // Subtract the last reading:
    total= total - readings[index];
    // Read from the sensor:
    readings[index] = analogRead(inputPin);
    // Add the reading to the total:
    total= total + readings[index];
    // Advance to the next position in the array:
    index = index + 1;

    // If we're at the end of the array...
    if (index >= numReadings) {
        // ...wrap around to the beginning:
        index = 0;
    }

    // Calculate the average:
    average = total / numReadings;
    // Send it to the computer as ASCII digits
    Serial.println(average);
    delay(1);    // Delay in between reads for stability
}
```

DISCUSS THE SKETCH:

We begin the adventure of smoothing data by declaring and initializing some variables:

```
const int numReadings = 10;

int readings[numReadings]; // The readings from the analog input
int index = 0;             // The index of the current reading
int total = 0;             // The running total
int average = 0;           // The average
int inputPin = A0;
```

Wonder why that first variable is a constant? To explain this take a look at the next variable declaration, it is the array we will use to store our sensor data. Notice that the size of this array is determined by the constant *numReadings*. Arduino will not allow any variable other than a constant integer to be used for array size declaration (otherwise you get an error). The reason for this is because every variable that is declared is allotted a specific amount of space in the microcontrollers memory. The same is true for arrays. If you could change the size of the array while the program is executing then nothing would stop you from accidentally running out of memory.

You can also hard code a number for the array size declaration - but I prefer a constant variable anyway.

The rest of the variables are straightforward, well named and commented.

The setup() of this sketch is much like any other, the standard Serial.begin() to start serial communications, but what is interesting is that we use a *for loop* to set all the elements in the array equal to zero.

```
for (int thisReading = 0; thisReading < numReadings; thisReading++) {
    readings[thisReading] = 0;
}
```

Take a look at *for loop* in this setup(). Do you remember the three components of the *for loop* header? [The *header* is the term that refers to the code inside parentheses following the word *for*.]

The first is the counter variable, then the condition and finally the incrementation. Each time through the loop we are setting an element in the array equal to zero – until all 10 elements are equal to zero and the array is initialized.

The real action happens in the loop(). Here is an overview of what the loop() will do (beware - this is going to sound like a lot, but we will be covering it step-by-step).

The loop() averages the readings that are stored in the *readings[]* array. To average the readings the variable *total* keeps a running tally of all the sensor values that are collected. Every time through the loop we replace one reading in the array with a new reading. To do this we subtract the old reading from the running total and then record and add the new reading. Finally we divide the total by the number of elements in the array to determine the average. Sound confusing? Let's take a look at the code:

```
// Subtract the last reading:
total=total - readings[index];
  0  =  0   -  0
```

The first time through the loop(), the variable's *total* and *index* are both equal to zero. We haven't even taken any sensor readings yet, so the readings[] array is filled with zeros. The calculation at this line of code boils down to:

⟶ 0 = 0 - 0

Not very exciting. For example, let's pretend that we already have ten readings in our array:

⟶ {5, 6, 8, 10, 6, 7, 7, 7, 9, 6}

If you add all of these values they equal 71. Let's also imagine the *total* variable is equal to 71.

If we look at that first line of code again, it basically says "take the current total and subtract the first element in the array, now save this as the new total":

```
total=total - readings[index];
 71 =  71  -  5     // The total variable now equals 66
```

Since the number 5 is the first value in the array the total now equals 66. Now let's record a new sensor reading to replace the value (5) that we just subtracted:

```
// Read from the sensor:
readings[index] = analogRead(inputPin);
```

The *index* variable is still equal to 0, this line of code places a new reading from the analog pin into the first element of the array. Now say the number 7 is the new value recorded by analogRead(). Therefore, the number 5 is replaced by the number 7. The array now contains these elements:

$$\longrightarrow \quad \{7, 6, 8, 10, 6, 7, 7, 7, 9, 6\}$$

The next step is to add this new sensor value (7) to the *total* variable.

```
// Add the reading to the total:
total=total + readings[index];
  66 =  66  +  7     // Total now equals 73
```

We take the *total* variable and add the 7 we just recorded and saved in the first element of the array. This step updates the *total* variable. This updated *total* variable needs to be divided by the number of elements in the array to determine the average.

Before we calculate the average let's increment the *index* variable by one. Now the next time through the loop(), the *index* variable will point to the second element in the *readings*[] array:

```
// Advance to the next position in the array:
index = index + 1;
```

To prevent the *index* variable from exceeding the number of elements in the array we use an *if statement*:

```
if (index >= numReadings) {
    // ...wrap around to the beginning:
    index = 0;
}
```

This statement says "If the value of *index* is equal to or greater than *numReadings* then set *index* back to zero." Recall that *numReadings* happens to be the size of the array – by enforcing this condition and resetting the count back to zero we prevent exceeding the index of the array.

Can we average already?! Yes - finally we calculate and send the average to the serial monitor:

```
// Calculate the average:
average = total / numReadings;
// Send it to the computer as ASCII digits
Serial.println(average);
```

Now, instead of seeing the raw values flash across the serial monitor, you should see a more consistent, non-jumpy value.

Let's recap the steps in the loop():

1 Subtract a value from the *total*

2 Record a new sensor value and put it in the array

3 Add the new sensor value from the array to the *total*

4 Increment the array *index* variable

5 Make sure the array index is within bounds with an *if statement*

6 Divide the *total* variable by the number of elements in the array to calculate the average

7 Print the average to the serial monitor

That's the scoop! These steps provide a smooth output. Increasing the elements in the array will increase the smoothing effect. Likewise, reducing the number of elements in the array will reduce the smoothing effect.

TRY ON YOUR OWN CHALLENGE:

- Adjust the variable *numReadings* and monitor the output – anticipate some problems with increasing or decreasing this value.

- Use the smoothed output to adjust the brightness of an LED at pin 9.

CHAPTER

06

ONE EXTRA

As you continue to increase your knowledge in programming and circuit design, you will find that there is always something more out there to learn and to apply. In many cases, new information will be an expansion upon a concept that you already know. This chapter covers matrices - an expansion of the array data structure.

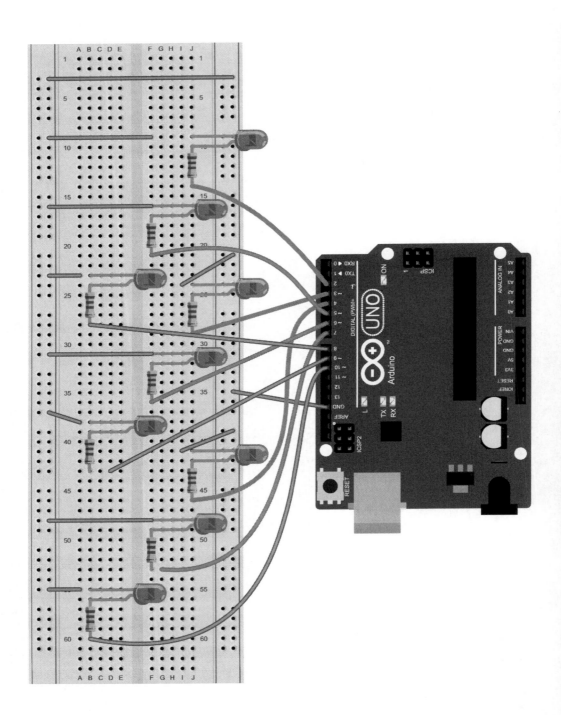

Multi-Dimensional Array AKA Matrix

KEY POINTS:

1 A *matrix* is indexed very much like an array. The rows are indexed first, and then the column is indexed as follows - myMatrix[rows][columns]

2 A *nested for loop* is simply one or more *for loops* inside the curly brackets of a *for loop*.

I don't know if you are into Zen or not – I don't know Zen from jack. When I think of Zen I think of how the organization of the outside world can effect the way I think and feel – I am sure this is way off – but that's about as far as I have cared to ponder.

If my shop is organized, if my computer files are organized, if my calendar is organized then my mind can be more organized. One might argue I wouldn't have time to build anything because I am too busy organizing!

What does this have to do with Arduino or matrices? Here is the angle I am taking – the more you can represent physical reality in storing data the easier it will be to think about and manipulate this data. What am I talking about?

Ok, say you are making a game for a carnival. People shoot Bluetooth guns at targets lined up in a row. When a player hits one, an Arduino actuates a servomotor to drop the target and increments a score board. Let's say you plan to use an array to store the condition of each of these targets – how would you represent them in the array?

One way would be to have them entered in the array from left to right – the left most target is the first element in the array and the right most target is the last element. This just makes sense – unless there is some very good reason to jumble the order of the targets, you would represent them in the array as they appear in the physical world.

Let's say you want to add multiple rows of targets, each above the other. Can you picture this? Imagine there are four rows of targets now, and each row has 5 individual targets – how could you represent this in an Arduino data structure?

A multi-dimensional array also know as a *matrix* – allows you to store data exactly that way.

We will take 9 LEDs and position them in the form of a matrix, which we will control with a multi-dimensional array. Please note that this is not an LED matrix in the traditional sense, which you may be familiar with. LED matrices are built and operated in a different manner – though they often employ multi-dimensional arrays.

YOU WILL NEED:

1 220 ohm resistors (9)

2 LEDs (9)

3 Jumper wires (18)

4 Cough drops (3) - Cherry flavored.

STEP-BY-STEP INSTRUCTION:

The trick here is to have 9 LEDs connected to pins 2 through 10. You need a 220 ohm resistor for each LED - it can get a bit packed on the Arduino headers!

1 From the Arduino run a jumper wire from the ground pin to the long ground rail of the breadboard.

2 Run another jumper wire from this ground rail to the ground rail on the opposite side of the breadboard.

3 Place an LED on the breadboard. Be sure the legs are in different rails.

4 Connect one end of a 220 ohm resistor to the same rail as the long leg of your LED.

5 Connect the other end of the 220 ohm resistor to a separate rail.

6 From pin 2, run a jumper wire to the 220-ohm resistor. Your breadboard should look like this:

7 Now repeat this process for the next LED, until you have three in a row, utilizing pins 2, 3 and 4.

8 Continue the process for the next row using pins 5, 6 and 7.

(9) Complete the circuit with the last row using pins 8, 9 and 10.

(10) Plug the Arduino into your computer.

(11) Open up the Arduino IDE.

(12) Open the sketch for this section.

(13) Click the Verify button (check mark icon). The Arduino IDE will check your code for errors.

(14) Click the Upload button (right arrow icon). You will see the TX and RX LEDs on your Arduino board begin to flash rapidly.

(15) Your LEDs should start doing cool things.

THE ARDUINO CODE:

```
/*
 * Multi-Dimensional Array AKA Matrix
 * This sketch demonstrates the use of a multi-dimensional
 * array to control 9 LEDs formed into a matrice.
 *
 * The circuit:
 * - 9 LEDs connected from pins 2 through 10 (through 220-Ohm
 *   resistors) to ground shaped into a 3 by 3 matrix.
 *
 * This example code is in the public domain.
 */


// The matrix will hold the pin assignments for the led
```

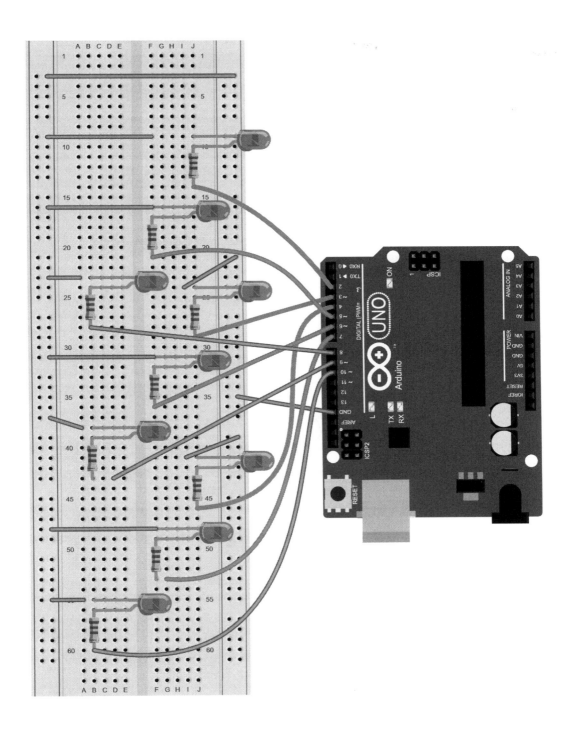

```
int pinMatrix[3][3] = {
    { 2, 3, 4 },
    { 5, 6, 7 },
    { 8, 9, 10 }
};



void setup() {
    // Use a nested for loop to initialize all the pins
    for (int i = 0; i < 3; i++){
        for (int j = 0; j < 3; j++){
            pinMode(pinMatrix[i][j], OUTPUT);
        } // Close for i
    } // Close for j
} // Close setup()



void loop() {
    // This nested for loop will turn each LED on and off in sequence
    for (int i = 0; i < 3; i++){
        for (int j = 0; j < 3; j++){
            digitalWrite(pinMatrix[i][j], HIGH);
            delay(100);
            digitalWrite(pinMatrix[i][j], LOW);
        } // Close for i
    } // Close for j
} // Close loop()
```

DISCUSS THE SKETCH:

The sketch begins by declaring and initializing one variable – a matrix. If you recall how to declare an array, you will notice its resemblance to a matrix declaration:

```
int pinMatrix[3][3] = {
    { 2, 3, 4 },
    { 5, 6, 7 },
    { 8, 9, 10 }
};
```

First we indicate what the matrix will hold – this matrix will hold integer values, so we use the int data type. Next we name the matrix. Since this matrix holds the digital pin numbers the LEDs are attached to, I named it *pinMatrix*. We follow the name by two sets of open and closing brackets. Inside the first bracket is the number of rows the matrix will have. Inside the second set of brackets is the number of columns the matrix will have.

The entire matrix and each individual row of the matrix is enclosed in curly brackets. Each row is separated by a comma. Notice that I have aligned each row of the matrix in the sketch as it appears on the breadboard layout. I could have done this declaration in a single line, but it is less readable in my opinion:

```
int pinMatrix[3][3] = {{ 2, 3, 4 },{ 5, 6, 7 },{ 8, 9, 10 }};
```

When you are setting the number of elements in the row and column you could use a variable, but it has to have the *constant* qualifier. For example, we could have written:

```
const int rows = 3;
const int cols = 3;
int pinMatrix[rows][cols] = {
                                { 2, 3, 4 },
                                { 5, 6, 7 },
                                { 8, 9, 10 }
                            };
```

This would have worked fine. This way you can expand the size by adjusting the constants at the top of your program. If you do not want to put values in the array yet, then you don't have to. You can just declare the array and initialize it later. That would look like:

```
int pinMatrix[rows][cols]; // No need to have values from the start
```

You must include the size of the rows and columns when you declare a multidimensional array.

If you ever forget which comes first, either rows or columns, a helpful trick to remember is to think "RC" - as in RC cars - that helps me at least!

The setup() of this sketch needs to accomplish one task - setting all the pins in the matrix as OUTPUTs. We use a nested *for loop* to do this. The nested *for loop* and the matrix are like tag team wrestlers – they work great together. Before we look at how the nested *for loop* works, let's talk about how a matrix is indexed.

Like arrays, matrices are zero indexed, so the first row in the matrix is 0, and the first column is 0. Consider this matrix:

```
matrix[3][3] = {
              { 2, 3, 4 },
              { 5, 6, 7 },
              { 8, 9, 10 }
      };
```

To reference the elements in the matrix we use the following index:

Matrix[0][0] would equal 2.

Matrix[0][1] would equal 3.

Matrix[1][2] would equal 7.

Matrix[2][2] would equal 10.

Get the gist? I know it can be confusing, since the size of the array is 3 by 3, but the indexing starts at 0. Once you get past the apparent weirdness of this, it becomes quite easy.

The following is my best attempt at explaining how we use the nested loop with this matrix – the process can be difficult to word - take a look at the diagrams before reading further to help clarify the process.

Basically the nested *for loop* says "Let's look at the first row of the matrix and work from left to right across the row setting each pin as an OUTPUT. Once we get to the last column, let's move on to the next row, and start back from left to right. Keep repeating this until we are out of rows." There is no better way to understand matrix reference and operations than trying some on your own!

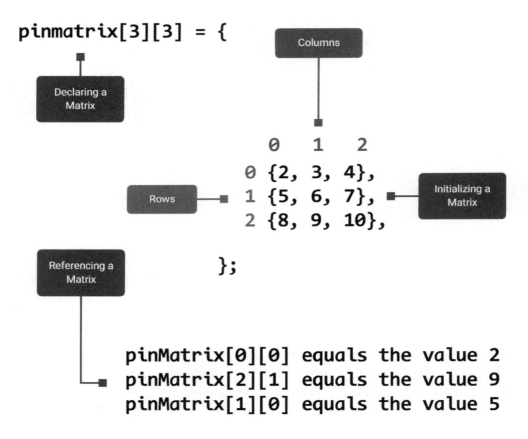

```
pinmatrix[3][3] = {
```

Declaring a Matrix

Columns

	0	1	2
0	{2,	3,	4},
1	{5,	6,	7},
2	{8,	9,	10},

Rows

Initializing a Matrix

```
};
```

Referencing a Matrix

```
pinMatrix[0][0] equals the value 2
pinMatrix[2][1] equals the value 9
pinMatrix[1][0] equals the value 5
```

Let's take a look at the nested *for loop* in the setup():

```
for (int i = 0; i < 3; i++){          // First loop
    for (int j = 0; j < 3; j++){      // Second loop
        pinMode(pinMatrix[i][j], OUTPUT); // Set current pin as OUTPUT
    } // Close for i
} // Close for j
```

Now, consider just the first *for loop*:

```
for (int i = 0; i < 3; i++)
```

We begin with $i = 0$ as the counter variable, we set the condition for the loop to continue as i being less than three, and then we increment i by one every time through the loop. The first *for loop* controls the rows of the matrix. The first time through the loop, i is equal to zero which references the first row in the matrix. What code do we execute when we start the first *for loop*? It's another *for loop*!

The next *for loop* looks exactly like the first, except that now we use the variable j as the counter variable. We will use j to reference the columns of the matrix. Now that the inner *for loop* is active, it will continue until its condition is met (that is j < 3). Since j initially equaled zero, this *for loop* will run three times. What code does this *for loop* execute?

It sets the modes of the pins, using pinMode(). Simple enough:

```
pinMode(pinMatrix[i][j], OUTPUT);
```

Do you see how pinMatrix[][] is referenced using *i* and *j*? The first time through the outer *for loop*, *i* equals zero, and *j* equals zero.

```
matrix[i][j] = {
              { 2, 3, 4 },
              { 5, 6, 7 },
              { 8, 9, 10 }
          };
```

Thus pinMatrix[0][0] is equal to 2.

Pin 2 is set as an OUTPUT by pinMode(). Now the inner *j* loop will run again – because it has not yet met its condition. So now *j* will equal 1 but *i* still equals zero. The pin mode will be set by pinMatrix[0][1] which references pin 3.

Again the inner loop will run and *j* will equal 2, so pinMatrix[0][2] will be executed which means pin 4 has been set as an OUTPUT. Now the condition of the inner *for loop* has been met, *j* cannot be incremented any further and the inner *for loop* is exited.

Now we start back at the outer loop. The *i* counter is incremented from 0 to 1. What is the first code that is executed in the outer *for loop*? It's just the inner *for loop* again. The inner *for loop* starts again from scratch, *j* equals 0. Now we look at the first element in the second row:

```
pinMatrix[1][0]
         i  j
```

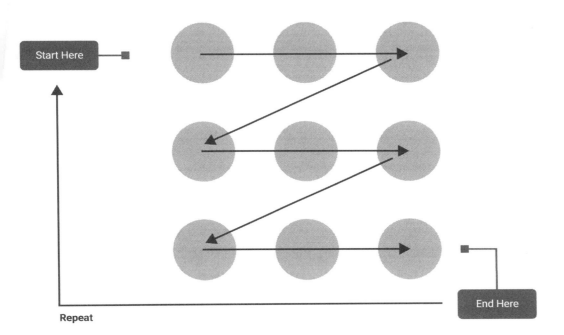

Start Here

End Here

Repeat

The inner *for loop* will continue through until its condition is met. Once the inner *for loop* is complete then the outer *for loop* will start one more time, allowing us to reference the third row of the matrix.

Once these two *for loops* have run their course, all the pins in the array will be set as OUTPUTs. This accomplishes the setup(). Let's move on to the loop().

The object of this sketch is to turn the LEDs on and off in sequence. We start at the top left of the matrix and move across the first row, and then starting on the second row from left to right and finally the third row.

Again we employ a nested *for loop* along with the code to turn an LED on and off.

```
// This nested for loop will turn each LED on and off in sequence
for (int i = 0; i < 3; i++){
    for (int j = 0; j < 3; j++){
        digitalWrite(pinMatrix[i][j], HIGH);
        delay(100);
        digitalWrite(pinMatrix[i][j], LOW);
    } // Close for i
} // Close for j
```

There is no difference between this nested *for loop* and the one used in the setup(). The only thing that has changed is what code is executed in the inner *for loop*. Instead of setting pinMode() we are using digitalWrite() and delay() to blink an LED on and then off, in sequence.

That's all this *for loop* wrote. Once the nested *for loops* are complete, the loop() starts again – thus giving us a continuous LED light show.

NOTE: This LED layout in the form of a matrix is operated differently than typical LED matrices you may be familiar with. Most LED matrices turn on and off the LEDs at a rapid pace to make it "look" like a constant image, when in fact all the LEDs are blinking very rapidly.

TRY ON YOUR OWN CHALLENGE:

- Instead of the LEDs blinking down the rows from left to right, can you make the LEDs blink down the columns from top to bottom?

- Can you reverse the direction of the blinking so that the lights go from right to left?

- Can you make an entire row blink at once and sequence down the rows from top to bottom?

CHAPTER

07

THE START OF A JOURNEY

My goal in this book was to start you on a journey toward developing your own projects - I hope you feel confident to move forward in whatever direction you choose.

Remember that Arduino is a community - and the community is the largest resource available to us all.

Not only should you use the resources others have made available, but also strive to be a resource for others.

Well, there you have it. By working through these examples you should have a basic understanding of how to hook things up to your Arduino and write code to make them work. I hope you noticed how often I linked to the Arduino Reference webpages:

http://arduino.cc/en/Reference/HomePage

Even after years of using Arduino I still frequently reference these pages for information about functions, data types and just about everything else. The reference is almost always the first place I turn when trying out something new with Arduino. For more topics on Arduino, like controlling different hardware such as servos, rotary encoders, etc. - you can check out the Programming Electronics Academy membership program:

https://programmingelectronics.com/

It is my sincere desire that you build the ultimate cool thing which you have in the back of your mind. In many cases the biggest barrier between your imagination and reality is your attitude. Trying can be difficult, but as you have demonstrated here the learning curve can be overcome.

Best of luck!

—Michael Cheich

Published — June, 2021